HEALING T

THE HURT MIND

HEALING THE HURT MIND

Christian Faith and Clinical Psychiatry

M. DAVID ENOCH

HODDER AND STOUGHTON
LONDON SYDNEY AUCKLAND TORONTO

British Library Cataloguing in Publication Data

Enoch, M. David
  Healing the hurt mind.
  1. Psychiatry
  2. Pastoral counselling
  I. Title
  616.89'1   RC480

ISBN 0 340 338970

To Joyce and Dafydd

CONTENTS

PART III   'WONDERFUL COUNSELLOR'

INTRODUCTION

This book as befitting its subject has been lived. Both Christian Faith and Clinical Psychiatry are based on facts, but to become alive they must be applied in living.

They constitute the two major concerns of the writer's life, having been a practising physician for thirty years and a practising Christian for even longer.

I am aware of the vast numbers of people suffering from mental illness, one in five people having some psychiatric treatment during the course of their lives; also of the ignorance, prejudice and fear associated with it. One of the aims of this book is to counter this ignorance and fear by informing the intelligent layman of the facts concerning the mentally ill and the great advances that have occurred in their treatment during the past thirty years.

Christians have special problems related to psychiatry and many feel very guilty when they suffer a breakdown and find it difficult to accept psychiatric treatment. This reluctance reflects a sad conflict between psychiatry and Christianity. Psychiatry has undoubtedly been looked at with great suspicion by churchmen. Another clear aim of this book is to try to bridge the gap, and to emphasise that conflict should give way to co-operation, for the sake of the victims: of those who suffer from mental and emotional illnesses. I point out the common ground while accepting that there are essential differences.

While emphasising the power of psychiatry to heal hurt minds and restore broken personalities, I acknowledge the limitations of psychiatry. In outlining these I accept that even after a long and apparently successful course of psychotherapy people remain dissatisfied and unhappy for their deepest needs have not been met. For complete healing to occur the spiritual factors must be taken into consideration; spiritual resources, such as prayer, the scripture and the fellowship used in the therapeutic process. Above all, the person must be introduced to 'The Wonderful Counsellor' by whose power alone we can be reconciled to God, and thus be 'ransomed, healed, restored, forgiven', to be made whole, for 'by His stripes we are healed.'

In view of the fact that for a long time I had had a foot in both camps, I was often requested to talk or write about the interrelationship between Christian Faith and Clinical Psychiatry but refrained from doing so because I did not think the time was ripe. An outstanding opportunity, however, arose in 1981 when Principal Dafydd Davies, Dean of Divinity of the University of Wales, kindly invited me to give the Edwin Stephen Griffiths Memorial Lectures at University College, Cardiff. The very enthusiastic response of the audiences encouraged me to consider re-writing them for publication. From the very beginning, Robert Warner and the staff of Hodder and Stoughton encouraged me to proceed, and have continued to advise and support me throughout the preparation of the manuscript for publication.

While I cannot name everyone who has assisted me, such as patients, chiefs, colleagues and fellow Christians, it is imperative that I thank Dr Colin Ogilvy for helping in correcting a large part of the manuscript and Mrs Irene Tierney and Mrs Joan Molyneux for patiently typing it. I am indebted to Mrs K Lutas, Librarian, for her assistance. I would also like to thank the Canon Roy Barker for encouraging me to get actively involved in Christian witness, leadership and healing.

My final hope is that the book will go a long way to allay anxiety concerning mental illness, remove a great deal of ignorance associated with it, and bring hope of help and healing to many.

I
THE HURT MIND

A. DISORDERS

1. PSYCHIATRY AND THE CHRISTIAN

Psychiatry or psychological medicine is an increasingly significant branch of medicine. During the last thirty years it has grown in influence by becoming more effective in diagnosing mental and emotional disorders and especially in treating them. Whereas previously madness meant inevitable incarceration in a large Victorian, Belsen-like mental hospital for years, if not a lifetime, now a mere trickle follows that path. The discovery of physical treatments, including potent, powerful drugs, together with the development of a new attitude towards mental illness, has brought about nothing short of a revolution. Men and women have been treated increasingly in the community, and those who have needed inpatient care have been admitted for a short period only, usually into units in general district hospitals.

Within those hospitals the doctors specialising in this branch of medicine have inevitably rubbed shoulders with other specialists and have contributed to the management of their patients, and hence there has been an increasing understanding and acceptance of the speciality.

It is significant that these patients do not constitute a small, odd group of people, but make up a vast problem comprising great numbers of people and a variety of illnesses. Half the hospital beds of the United Kingdom are filled with patients suffering from mental disorders, 60 per cent of people attending G.P. surgeries suffer from emotional or psychological illnesses, and one in ten persons will have treatment for a mental illness sometime in the course of their lives. No person or family is immune. Mental illness is very democratic. It attacks all and is no respecter of class, creed, person or family.

The very nature of mental illness does cause great fear and shame. Though this is understandable, much, nevertheless, has arisen because of ignorance and fear. There is universal fear of 'going mad' for nothing is so frightening as disintegration of personality. We must accept that these illnesses, with their disordered thoughts and feelings and behaviour, can be frightening. They also overlap the spheres of belief and faith. Christians who suffer from mental illness find it particularly difficult to accept, are often bewildered and baffled by their condition, and accompanying this there may be a feeling of guilt.

As a psychiatrist of over twenty-five years' experience and a Christian for an even longer period, I have had a foot in both camps and seen travail and conflict in the minds and hearts of Christians who have been unfortunate enough to suffer in this way. Their plight has been aggravated by other Christians, including leaders such as clergymen and pastors, who have indicated clearly that they have no time for psychiatry and psychiatrists. Indeed, some have suggested that an alliance between priest and psychiatrist is unholy and that psychiatry is completely unacceptable to them. An extreme example of this opposition is reflected in the words of one such clergyman who said that psychiatry is surely of the devil.

It is not surprising, therefore, that Christians who do suffer from severe emotional disturbance with an accompanying depression or guilt feel it difficult to allow themselves to be referred to a psychiatrist for help and treatment. Several good Christians needing such help have expressed their unwillingness to accept it because of their reluctance to believe that they are ill and that it is appropriate for them as Christians to receive psychiatric help. They feel that it is a weakness and unacceptable for them as Christians to feel depressed or guilty and they find it difficult to reconcile this with their standing as Christians. There is still considerable reluctance, even among Christians, to accept a mental disorder as an illness needing proper, adequate treatment. As a result, more than one life has been lost. Suicidal, severe depression can be the lot of the Christian just as any other person. The saintly, Christian man whom I treated for a number of years always lost his faith and ability to pray when his depression got severe. It was one of my roles as his therapist to reassure him in the depths of his depression that his faith and the power to pray would return when his depressive illness had cleared, and this is what always occurred.

Faith and psychiatry inevitably meet at many points. There is much overlapping. This is true of medicine and religion as a whole and is particularly true of psychological medicine and the Christian faith. This applies on the conceptual as well as the practical level. For both deal with the basic thoughts and feelings for man and these in turn affect and dictate behaviour which is also the concern of both religion and psychiatry.

The aim of this book is to move along the borderland of faith and psychiatry, to clarify the problem areas and, by enriching the knowledge of one for the other, to gain a greater mutual insight and respect. Indeed, faith and psychiatry are complementary and need each other. How refreshing it would be to erase conflict and to establish a rapport between them for the ultimate good of the people whom they both try to serve. One leading churchman has described psychiatry as a new religion of the age and psychiatrists as new priests of a new religion. Psychiatry has not and never can usurp the role of Christian faith. It does deal with man in great depth but, even after the most successful therapy, man can remain unhappy and unfulfilled unless his spiritual needs are met. He remains restless till he finds his peace in God and in God alone. Never would we advocate a takeover bid, for not only would it be unworthy, it would be bound to fail. Christian faith remains supreme and no amount of psychological belief will take its place; it is through faith in Jesus Christ, the son of the living God alone, that man achieves wholeness and salvation.

Christians, therefore, should view psychiatry with less suspicion and less fear. This can be achieved by greater knowledge, for to gain insight is to become less fearful. When we view a tree through the mist it looks big and menacing, its branches about to devour us, yet when the sun breaks through the mist clears and we see a tree of just proportions whose branches are like welcoming arms, ready to give us shade and succour. So can psychiatry be: not a menacing, new theology which does away with the Christian faith but a system of ideas and facts which can directly help by application in the clinical setting in the alleviation, and sometimes the cure, of psychological and emotional illness.

In the first part of this book I shall look upon the hurt mind in many of its aspects, acknowledge the vastness and variety of the conditions and disturbances we meet, and note the problems of special concern to the Christian. Modern treatments and problems inherent in their use will be described in some detail.

In ending this introduction, I am moved to ask those who do have a grave suspicion of psychiatry and psychiatrists: from where do they believe the ability and knowledge of the psychiatrist emanate? Are not his ability and knowledge – and, indeed, the very drugs he discovers and uses – from God? Are they not merely discoveries from within the creation of the Creator, already present in God's world but brought forth to help in the alleviation of suffering? This is a vast problem affecting a great number of people from all shades of life who at some time or another suffer from mental, psychological and emotional disturbances of many different kinds. Indeed, there are as many psychiatric disorders as there are physical illnesses. They vary in severity of the symptoms and suffering they cause, in their natural history, in response to treatment and in their presentation. I shall now describe the commoner conditions, some of which are mild and cause little suffering while others are so severe that they cause total disintegration of a personality and ruin the life, not only of the patient, but often of the family to whom he or she belongs.

2. BREAKDOWNS

We accept even as Christians that people do have nervous breakdowns. We say people suffer from 'nerves'. By this we mean they suffer from a mild mental or emotional illness, but even if it is such a mild mental illness, we never proclaim the fact from the rooftops. We certainly do not collect with family and friends at the foot of the patient's bed and steal the patient's grapes as we do when visiting a patient after appendicectomy.

But it's just about acceptable – 'It's the strain and the stress, you know'. He or she has to be off work – not quite coping, but we console ourselves and others by saying, 'It's nothing much; nothing a few days' rest won't cure.'

The free-floating anxiety which the victim experiences usually comes on quite quickly and suddenly. He or she tries to shake it off, accepts that it is silly to feel like this and that there is no real cause for it, except perhaps a bit of overwork. But it becomes harder to accept and to tolerate when one's heart begins to flutter. We feel tension pains across the chest. Even worse symptoms may cause greater distress when he or she may have choking sensations in the throat and feelings of sensations in the head. 'Is this really an anxiety neurosis, Doctor? Can all these physical symptoms be explained on the basis of a neurotic illness?'

Anxiety state or anxiety neurosis is a very common cause of the so-called 'nervous breakdown'. One in six persons in the United Kingdom will suffer from some form of neurotic illness needing treatment during the course of their lives. They are regarded as *mild* emotional or psychological disorders in contradistinction to the more severe insanities or psychoses. The patient maintains insight, knows what is what, feels unwell, yet keeps in touch with reality and knows what is happening in the world around. Often, however, they will ask, 'Am I going mad, Doctor?' and the psychiatrist can in almost every case reassure them that they are not going out of their minds, not becoming mad, while accepting that they do feel anxious and ill.

Neuroses are illnesses. One has to admit that even some doctors find it difficult to accept this fact, let alone the general public. Hence, unfortunately, there is often lack of sympathy, not only from families and friends, but from doctors and others who should know better. There is, in spite of the oft-accompanying physical or somatic symptoms, no physical condition underlying the illness. Yet it is no mere figment of imagination. There may be no cancerous lump in the throat, but the choking sensation is very real and frightening. It is due to muscular tension and will clear when these muscles relax. The patient can be reassured that it is reversible though suffering may be great during the acute phase.

The anxiety is an experience of fear, of various degrees, an unpleasant emotion which spreads from mere anxiety to severe fear and panic, often accompanied by restlessness and irritability leading to an inability to concentrate – again very real psychological and emotional symptoms. The young student on reading the examination paper becomes paralysed with fear – the questions are quite unexpected, he has little of the knowledge necessary to answer them, and even that he cannot recall. Within half an hour after the examination ends he recalls all the facts he could not remember. His memory returns, for the paralysing anxiety-fear – examination nerves – has cleared.

Where such psychological and physical symptoms develop, the patients are undoubtedly suffering and ill. They suffer and are in pain, they have symptoms which affect their life-style, they can't carry on with their daily living and often cannot work effectively. Ignorant and insensitive people lack sympathy and understanding and thereby do these patients great disservice. So often others will say, 'Pull yourself together', but that is just what they cannot do, much as they would like to. The victims know that the anxiety is morbid and irrational, but they are prisoners of their own feelings.

Christians suffer from anxiety states just as other people; their faith does not make them immune. True Christians should hear the Master's call, 'Be not anxious', but we are such poor disciples. We fall short so often because we are in this world and are taken up with the stresses of so-called modern living. We get involved with the world, accept the standards of the world and suffer the same stresses as the non-Christian, both at home and at work. Christians do crack up and suffer neurotic reactions such as anxiety states. They should accept that these are illnesses and not feel more guilty than others. Indeed, even so-called Christian living may itself bring about particular stresses. The clergyman's wife who takes on duties within and outside the home must be ready to listen and to console at any hour of the day while herself bearing the responsibility of home, husband and children. The load is heavy and anxiety may well become a burden so great that a breakdown ensues.

When Christians have difficulty in accepting that they break down in this way, they may be helped by the parallel of physical illness. Neurotic breakdowns need specific forms of treatment just as much as pneumonia, a broken bone or even a cancer. Anxiety neurosis can be treated successfully in the short term with anti-tension drugs such as the famous Librium and Valium, together with supportive psychotherapy. It must be emphasised that this applies to Christians just as to anyone else. We shall deal later with the causes of anxiety states and other neurotic conditions and also with treatment and the special problems that arise in the case of Christians.

Anxiety neurosis is only one of the main neurotic conditions that we have to face. Others are obsessional neurosis or obsessive compulsive neurosis, hysterical neurosis and neurotic depression.

There is an important sub-group of anxiety states, namely phobic states, in which anxiety is focused on a specific fear or phobia such as a fear of spiders, or of authority figures, or a more general fear of open spaces, called agoraphobia, or of closed spaces, claustrophobia. In theory, many things could be the basis of our phobias but in fact there are few, and notable among these are the fear of animals, of certain kinds of personality such as an authoritative figure, of sickness or of death and the fear of harming somebody. In all these phobias there is an underlying anxiety but, because the fear is focused on a specific thing, it is more amenable to treatment by behavioural therapy.

Other Breakdowns

Obsessional Neurosis

Rituals and obsessive ideas are the chief symptoms of the obsessional neurosis. As such they are of interest to the religious, for ritual and repetitive thoughts are an integral part of religious conduct. When do obsessions (ideas which are forced into consciousness) or compulsions (forced acts) constitute an illness? It is when the ideas protrude into consciousness and the person cannot rid himself of them, though he knows that they are useless thoughts.

Though such ideas could, like phobias, be limitless, in reality only a few ideas are usually implicated. Common among these are thoughts of harming loved ones and obsessions about dirt and death. The acts which arise from compulsions are also limited in number and include checking things over and over again or washing ceaselessly. Yet these symptoms are similar to anxiety symptoms in that they can't be brushed aside. The victims cannot talk themselves out of these feelings which make life miserable, restrict personal activity and cause difficulty in carrying out work and preserving relationships with others. These obsessional symptoms do come and go; there may be periods of months or even years of freedom but usually they recur and may become so severe as to cause the patient great distress and despondency.

The reader may be reassured that obsessional traits do occur in so-called normal people; such people are often very meticulous in all that they do, tend to check things repeatedly and are regarded as perfectionists by those with whom they live. If we have such traits we need not worry unduly if they are under control. Most professional people such as clergy and doctors have obsessional traits – and indeed they need them to survive such a long period of training with repeated examinations and interviews under strict specified conditions. These traits can be of benefit and are essential for the pursuance of certain professions. Only a small percentage of obsessional personalities do break down under stress into an obsessional neurosis.

Hysterical States

Hysterical neurosis is arguably the most fascinating of the neuroses. Men, or should I say women, have always used hysterical mechanisms to deal with stress. The layman without quite understanding the remark will often have turned to the woman acting in a dramatic fashion under stress and said, 'Oh, you're being hysterical.' The person – not always a female – facing conflict often buried in the unconscious will convert it into apparently irrational behaviour and symptoms. These may be psychological and/or physical.

The man who had just been informed of the sudden death of his brother in a road accident immediately lost his memory. The young mother facing the pressure of bringing up five young children and unable to cope developed paralysis of her legs. Neither the man nor the young mother had any physical disease. The man has no injury or infection of his brain yet the function of his brain, i.e. the memory, becomes suddenly and massively defective. The young mother has no physical lesion in her legs or nervous system yet she has a very physical symptom – she cannot walk.

Neither will recover health and neither will become whole until their basic problems have been faced and dealt with. No amount of physical treatments will help. It is useless to be angry and to confront these patients with the 'fact' that their illness has no physical basis. If we do confront them and say that 'there is nothing wrong with you' it will only make matters worse. The man must gently and gradually be made to

accept the fact of his brother's death and all that it entails and
be helped to overcome the mental trauma of such news. The
young mother must be supported in the demands made by her
young family and be persuaded to believe in herself as one
capable of coping. Thus the motives for the hysterical behaviour will be removed and there will be no longer a need to
convert difficulties into symptoms.

Hysterical states are neurotic conditions; that is, there are
physical and psychological symptoms without any organic or
physical basis. They arise from unconscious conflicts and
difficulties which are not fully accepted. These can suddenly
cause great mental trauma and physical suffering and affect
the whole life of the person as well as other members of the
family.

The hysterical mechanism is not only used in the complete
hysterical neurosis, it is also used by other neurotic personalities who tend to be histrionic in their behaviour and act in an
excessive manner in order to gain their own way. I am sure
that every reader knows of one or two in their own family
group and may well have used such mechanisms themselves
under stress to gain their own way. Even where there is a basic
physical illness, people may exaggerate their symptoms to
gain greater sympathy and attention. Hence physicians often
say that in addition to the physical illness there is an 'hysterical overlay'. Perhaps 'hysterical overlay' is a label too frequently used by physicians to describe a patient who is
difficult and obstructive, yet at times it is a real phenomenon
which occurs in patients with hysterical personalities.

Christian groups often attract such personalities and under
the influence of a large congregation they may well exhibit
hysterical behaviour. At times it is difficult to distinguish the
real from the false, and to determine whether behaviour is
truly disinhibited and under the influence of the Holy Spirit,
or whether it is the hysterical reaction of a narcissistic
egocentric personality. It is a help to have the power of
discernment – itself a gift of the spirit – and to be reminded
that the Holy Spirit is a spirit of discipline and order.

There is a tendency for some hysterics to eat up the time

and energy of other people and make great demands upon them when it is obvious that this will not be sufficient for their needs nor effective in their treatment. Later we shall discuss the question of managing and treating neurotic conditions and shall emphasise the dangers of a malignant hysteric who will demand time and attention from individuals in the congregation and yet show no response whatsoever even after hours of counsel over a long period.

Diagnosing Neurotic Depression

There is one other important neurotic condition, neurotic depression, sometimes called reactive depression, which will be dealt with in the next section. There is, however, one more point to be made concerning the neurotic breakdowns. Whereas anxiety neurosis, phobic states, obsessional neurosis and neurotic depression can occur in 'pure form' with symptoms so clear as to make the diagnosis obvious, often there is a mixed picture with, for example, symptoms of anxiety and depression occurring together, and in those instances it would be fair to term the condition as a mixed neurotic reaction with anxiety and depressive symptoms. Patients and relatives often demand a diagnosis. Sometimes it is difficult to make one, but a provisional diagnosis made according to the facts before us is not only reassuring to the patient but also is the first step in the proper management and treatment of these conditions.

Diagnosis is very much part of the doctor's world, but others during the course of the last few years have suggested it is more important to counsel and to treat than to make an accurate diagnosis. However, to start treatment before making a diagnosis may lead to utter disaster.

Is the headache neurotic or physical? If physical, is it an infection or a tumour? Of course it is of paramount importance to know. Hence the need for doctors to deal with neurotic conditions and at the very beginning to differentiate between the physical and the psychological. This is one of my fears of the great growth in counselling movements in this country and elsewhere: that people will be taken on for counselling when they have a physical lesion needing appropriate treatment rather than a neurotic condition which the counsellor believes arises from tension or stress.

There is no substitute for the correct label, for diagnosis is the first step to effective treatment and sometimes the physician alone is able to meet this need. So often in my experience patients referred to as being neurotic, even by other doctors, turn out to have physical lesions. Only too often, these patients are referred because they are destructive and difficult and provoke the anger of the physicians who are dealing with them. But difficult patients and those with neurotic symptoms can also have physical illness, not least a malignant disease.

Depression
Normal people's moods fluctuate. The majority of us have our ups and downs. The 'down' is a depressive mood. If this sticks and deepens and there is no way of talking yourself out of it, then you have a depressive symptom which may well be part of a depressive illness.

Depression is the most common illness confronting doctors today. The illness can vary in degree of severity. Some are mild and transient and clear with a little reassurance. Others persist and need more intensive treatment including drug therapy combined with intensive psychotherapy. It is generally accepted that there are two main kinds of depressive illness, though there is much debate as to whether these are two distinct entities or are merely the extreme ends of the same spectrum. Certainly there appears to be a difference in both quality and quantity of symptoms and in the response to treatment.

Neurotic Depression
Neurotic depression or reactive depression is regarded as a less serious illness than the so-called endogenous depression or the depressive component of the manic-depressive psychosis, but it must be made clear that neurotic depression also can be severe and dangerous. However, neurotic depression occurs in a personality who has tended to show depressive

traits for most of their life and there is more often than not a discernible precipitant factor, though it does not mean that if this is removed the depression automatically clears. There is a persisting feeling of sadness and misery and an inability to feel happy or joyous, whatever the situation or however much encouragement and reassurance are given. The depressive mood is significantly worse as the day goes on and pressures build up and, for housewives, it is especially prominent in the early evenings when the family returns home from work or school with their problems and demands. Linked with the depressive mood is a great deal of underlying anxiety and a lack of ability to concentrate and to cope with the simple tasks of daily life. Allied to these will often be loss of sleep and in particular a difficulty in going off to sleep – an initial insomnia. In addition, the person may well be off his food, tense and anxious and also unable to concentrate and carry out simple tasks.

Endogenous Depression
Endogenous depression, as its name suggests, is a depression 'from within', rather than from the environment. The depressive mood is worse in the mornings and typically improves as the day goes on. This diurnal variation in mood, which the patient will describe clearly, is a very prominent feature of this kind of depressive illness as is persistent early morning waking. The patient complains that his sleep is fitful, that he wakes at two or three in the morning and is unable to go back to sleep.

Consider, therefore, a man who is very depressed, who wakes persistently at 3 a.m. and is unable to go back to sleep, and who also has feelings of guilt, despondency and despair regarding his future. His appetite is very poor and he will have lost a lot of weight. Hence he may feel fearful of his health. Life will be an abject misery. He sees no light in the gloom, he is in utter despair. At this point, it is no wonder that he feels suicidal and indeed may kill himself. As the depression becomes more profound, he begins to believe that he faces eternal damnation, that everybody is against him and that he should be punished for his wrong-doings. These feelings of persecution, of paranoid ideas, alienate him further from his fellows. He is concerned that he is causing great suffering to his family and that they have come to this sorry pass because of him. He often speaks of the depression as a black cloud which has descended on him and of a heaviness through which he tries to walk with his burden of depression and guilt. This feeling is reflected in poverty of movement, or 'retardation'; there is both physical and mental slowing and yet at the same time he may be very anxious within, restless and agitated and unable to find peace anywhere or with anybody.

So often this kind of depression descends upon the middle-aged man with exemplary character, a perfectionist who has given his life in the service of others, his family, his work or profession, or his church. Suddenly the cloud of depression descends and his thinking, feeling and behaviour are totally coloured by the blackness of this despairing mood. This often explains the surprising suicide of a good, well-known man or woman which provokes the cry: 'Why did he of all people kill himself?'

The natural history of this awful illness used to be one of persistence and deepening for two years or so. Improvement would then begin, but often the patient would have been incarcerated in one of the old mental hospitals. If he did show a measure of recovery, he would now be suffering not only from depression but the apathy of institutionalisation. The family meanwhile would have built up an alternative life for themselves and he would no longer be included in their plans. Indeed, he himself would have no great expectations and when recovery took place, as already implied, institutionalisation would have taken its toll.

With the advent of the wonderful group of antidepressant drugs in the mid 1950s, a revolution has occurred in the treatment of these severe depressive illnesses, especially those with endogenous features. Of those patients given adequate regular treatment with antidepressant drugs and reassuring psychological support, 85 per cent recover within two to three months. 'Are they cured?' The majority are, in that the symptoms clear and they are able to return to their family and job and to lead a full active life. A few have a recurrence and this is similarly treated, but if there are more than two attacks, long-term therapy with drugs must be considered. A very small percentage do not recover and some residual symptoms persist. These patients may need treatment with a combination of drugs and probably electrical treatment or deep psychotherapy.

The change in outlook for these patients since the advent of effective drugs cannot be overemphasised. I personally had the privilege of practising when there were no such drugs available and then saw their introduction and witnessed their great effectiveness. They remove severe symptoms, bring back hope and save lives. This is equally true of Christians as of non-Christians, of patients with religious beliefs and those without religious beliefs. Christians of all denominations have come to me from all over the country with depressive illnesses, but this is not surprising when we realise that the great saints of every age have had profound episodes of dark depression.

I am aware that problems arise regarding drug-taking and other forms of treatment for depressive illnesses. These will be discussed in detail when we deal later with the treatment under the appropriate section. Meanwhile, suffice it to explain that depressive illness is a common illness from which many Christians suffer. The very nature of the symptoms such as guilt, despair and hopelessness makes it particularly distressing for the Christian. Yet psychiatric treatment can cure, or at least relieve, in the vast majority of cases.

Problems of guilt in taking drugs should not hinder any Christians or non-Christians from having treatment which will bring them out from black despair to glorious hope, from lack of faith to a faith-filled life, from despair to joy, from death to life. I realise that some criticise psychiatrists for giving too little time to their patients. I am not saying that drugs are solely the answer but, from the controlled experiments that I have seen pass before my eyes, I know that they have fundamentally changed the treatment of depressive illness.

I believe that if someone is suffering from severe endogenous depression and has not received the appropriate antidepressant, then this amounts to negligence on the part of whoever has been in charge of his treatment. Of course I would add that drug giving alone is not sufficient. Emotional support and sometimes deeper analysis into the causes of the depression may be necessary in order to avoid a recurrence, but first things first. Again I say, in the case of the endogenous depression, the treatment of choice is the appropriate antidepressants given by a sympathetic doctor.

The saintly Christian I referred to in an earlier chapter, when he suffered from severe endogenous depression with marked feelings of guilt and unworthiness, inability to pray and loss of faith, had to be treated with the appropriate antidepressant drug. After a few weeks his symptoms cleared and his faith and power to pray returned. Of course, during those weeks I saw him, I talked to him in depth and tried to reassure him, but there is no doubt that it was the drugs which were effective. Without them, he would have taken years to recover or might not have recovered at all.

During one part of my career, I felt that even deep depression should be treated solely with psychotherapy and took it on myself to treat four or five such depressives in this way, but in each case we had to revert to antidepressants in order to acquire full recovery. There should be no battle between drugs and psychotherapy for both are needed. Dozens, if not hundreds, of patients known to me have recovered from one episode of depression, following treatment with drugs and supportive psychotherapy, and have had no recurrence of their illness. There are, of course, people prone to depression who have recurrences of the depressive illness and who need constant treatment both with drugs and psychotherapy.

3. INSANITIES

The severe depression which I described in the last section was called endogenous depression. This is a form of psychosis in which the patient is so severely depressed that he despairs of himself and his future. Often accompanying this will be an equally destructive belief that he is poverty stricken, and allied to these desperate feelings are the ideas of suicide. He thus can be regarded as lacking insight and divorced from the true state of affairs. He is suffering from a depressive psychosis – an insanity.

On the other hand, the patient may become 'high', his mood so uplifted that he will be constantly euphoric whatever the state he finds himself in and whatever the problems facing him. He may well consider himself to be the greatest of men, with superhuman powers. He will act so, speaking non-stop about numerous subjects in a matter of a few minutes. He will be overactive, so much so that he will ask his wife to cook him a meal but on receiving it will not be able to find time to sit down to eat it. The euphoria consists of extreme joyous feelings, reaching at times to ecstasy. This will be rather superficial, for if anyone crosses him he will show considerable irritability and become very angry. He may erroneously believe that he has great plans for himself and his family, that he has great possessions or that he holds a high position in society.

He is, in other words, so 'high' that he lacks insight into his true condition. He is again divorced from the reality of the situation in which he finds himself. He suffers from mania. Such patients may have one such episode during the course of their lives, others may have several. If the manic episode is followed by an episode of severe depression of the kind that I have described earlier as endogenous depression, then the patient will be said to be suffering from the classic, well-known condition called manic-depressive psychosis.

This psychosis is a severe form of mental disorder in which the whole of the personality is affected, the symptoms are very severe and the patient is regarded as 'mad' in that he lacks insight into his condition and is divorced from reality. Usually the condition is easily recognisable but sometimes the symptoms are covered up and do not reveal themselves at once. Eventually, however, they are revealed, either in thought or deed, and then there is no doubt that the patient is insane. Mania, endogenous depression and manic-depressive psychosis are the madnesses of mood. Primarily the disorder is within the feelings of the person but it may be severe enough to extend into the realms of thought and behaviour. Both these are also affected in a severe way. Though mood disorders are regarded as functional psychoses, that is insanities without an organic basis, they do affect the physical wellbeing of the patient in a very serious way.

Often accompanying a severe endogenous depression is a considerable loss of weight over a comparatively short period. Some depressives look so ill that one has to consider the differential diagnosis of carcinoma of the bronchus or stomach, especially in middle-aged men presenting with severe depression and considerable loss of weight. Again, mania or the manic phase of a manic-depressive psychosis is a threat to physical health and often cardiovascular changes occur to threaten the very life of the person. These are additional reasons why these conditions must be diagnosed as quickly as possible and treated thoroughly by both physical and psychological means. It is difficult to comprehend how the physician in psychological medicine can be set aside in such conditions.

Often there is criticism of the way that psychiatrists deal with people suffering from mood disorders, especially depressive illnesses. In particular, the complaint is based on the fact that they are given only a short time, sometimes only five to ten minutes, with the psychiatrist and then perhaps only once every four or six weeks. This, in many ways, is an unfair criticism, for initially psychiatrists will give the time necessary to make the proper diagnosis and subsequently will give them the necessary support. Again we must emphasise that drugs in these kinds of mood psychoses are an essential part of treatment and no one, except the physician in this branch of medicine, can make the proper diagnosis and prescribe the proper drugs. We shall deal with the particular drugs that are indicated in the chapter on treatments, but, apart from drugs, it is vital to support the patients during the course of their acute illness and to continue this support later, allowing them to talk about their problems and their symptoms. The psychological aspects of treatment are an essential ingredient of the management of such cases, but these alone are not sufficient and people who suggest that these depressive illnesses may be cured without drugs are doing such patients great disservice, if not a great deal of potential harm.

These mood disorders require drugs just as other conditions with a physical basis. It would be tragic, indeed one would be open to the charge of negligence, if somebody suffering from thyrotoxicosis were not given the appropriate drug. Again, the diabetic would be more than foolish if, on the advice of any well-meaning person, he discontinued taking his daily injections of insulin. Equally, depressive illnesses need antidepressant drugs yet some people, even Christians, are reluctant to accept this and so put the health of the patient in jeopardy.

Schizophrenias

The schizophrenias constitute another major group of insanities. Rather surprisingly, schizophrenia is a common, malignant illness of the young, rearing its ugly head between the ages of sixteen and twenty-two years, both in males and females, though twice as many of the former have it, and together one in every hundred persons in the United Kingdom suffers from the illness. The public at large, who know schizophrenia as the 'split mind', mistakenly believe that Dr Jekyll and Mr Hyde is an example of such a condition. Dr Jekyll and Mr Hyde, however, is an example of multiple personalities, the underlying mechanism being an hysterical one, as described in the sub-section on hysterical states. The so-called 'split' in schizophrenia refers to the division between the ideas and the mood. The patient at times thinks sad thoughts and yet will be laughing. This is also known as incongruity of mood, a major symptom of a schizophrenic illness. It may be that the patient will also show a flattening of mood. This is linked often with introversion and autism where the young person will be preoccupied with his own morbid thoughts and withdraw from the world around. He will be reluctant to talk, and those around him will find it difficult to communicate with him. He will have little spontaneous speech and will give the impression that there is a glass wall around him.

Typically there is disordered thought. Speech, or at least part of it, will be irrelevant and nonsensical. The ideas expressed will not connect properly and some of the meanings of the speech will be difficult to comprehend. Initially this may not be easy to elicit, but will become more obvious with the progress of the illness. Eventually speech may become totally irrelevant and nonsensical and the patient will make up words and phrases which are not used in normal language. This is known as *word salad* and is a reflection of the severity of the thought disorder and the disintegration that has occurred.

In addition, there may well be distinct delusions; the patient will have false beliefs impervious to reason. He will, for example, believe that people are plotting against him or that some members of his family are trying to poison him. Any amount of argument to the contrary will not make him change his mind one iota. He may well be hallucinated. He will have sensations, either visual or auditory, without adequate sensory stimulation. He will say that he hears voices from outside his head that speak about him, though there will be no one around to do so. He will state that people can read his thoughts and can describe what he is thinking. The 'voices' that he hears, usually in the third person, talk in a critical manner about him. When visual hallucinations are present the patient will say that he sees visions and faces or other images when there is no basis in fact.

It is significant that Bleuler, who first described this condition, gave a remarkable description and called it dementia praecox, believing that it was a dementing process occurring in the young. This suggested that the brain itself was damaged and that the thought processes deteriorated progressively until the patient became confused and demented. Later this idea was found to be totally mistaken, for no such intellectual deterioration takes place in schizophrenia, though the illness causes difficulty of thought, which in the acute phase in particular gives the impression that the patient is 'confused' and in a dementing condition. If one concluded that this process would be progressive, then one can see why Bleuler initially believed that this was a dementia occurring in a young age group.

However, the illness does cause a downward drift in the life of the victim, sometimes intellectually and often socially; for example, an undergraduate schizophrenic might deteriorate to such an extent as not to be able to continue his studies. Some schizophrenics, however, recover sufficiently to return to continue with their degree courses. The prognosis of the schizophrenias has been fundamentally changed since the advent of the miraculous phenothiazines and other antipsychotic drugs in the mid 'fifties. Now we expect the drugs at least to dampen down, if not clear, the symptoms. Two-thirds of those given antipsychotic medication recover sufficiently to return to live a full life. A third do not respond well and these usually have to be satisfied with leading a lower standard of life. It is from this group that the social drifters come.

It is still doubtful if we can regard successful treatment of the schizophrenias with drugs as a cure, but they certainly can cause the symptoms to clear almost completely. It does seem necessary, however, that the drug be continued in some form, either orally or by injection, for some considerable time, if not indefinitely, if improvement is to be maintained. More details will be given about this in the section on treatments.

Schizophrenia is traditionally subdivided into four groups, simple, hebephrenic, catatonic and paranoid. The term simple schizophrenia must not mislead us because, although in this condition there is an absence of gross, initial behaviour disturbance, the most prominent features being a flattening of affect and general lethargy, it can be one of the most malignant of the subgroups. Hebephrenic schizophrenia, which has been seen less and less during the past ten or fifteen years, presents with a considerable degree of disturbance of personality; the patient becomes giggly and disinhibited as well as markedly deluded. The catatonic schizophrenic can show extremes of behaviour, either becoming totally withdrawn or becoming extremely excited, even to the point of ecstasy. Paranoid schizophrenia is a more common type of the subgroups where there is quite a degree of preservation of the personality and where delusions of a paranoid nature and hallucinations are prominent.

In view of the fact that mania, as already mentioned, and schizophrenia can lead to ecstasy states in which much of the thought disorder contains religious, philosophical material, they have been dubbed as 'religious manias'. The term suggests that too much religion has caused this madness. This is a complete fallacy. There is no such thing as a religious mania. There can be insanities where religious material is present and colours the content of thought but this does not justify the label of religious mania, which implies that religion is the basis of the condition.

There is another situation where there can be some difficulty in differentiating between insanity such as schizophrenia and some religious behaviour experience such as conversion. Two cases exemplify this difficulty that can face the clinician psychiatrist.

A young man of a religious family suddenly expressed the view that he had experienced a religious conversion. He became preoccupied with the reading of the scriptures and prayer but his behaviour became so extreme and bizarre that his close relatives, though very happy at the thought of his being converted, were forced to consider the possibility that he was ill. After close detailed examination I had to conclude that the family's suspicions were justified and that he was suffering from a schizophrenic illness. The parents on being told this were sad, yet relieved, and understood that the most important thing for him and the family was to have the right diagnosis and proceed with the proper treatment.

The second case poses the same problem but had a different result. The patient was a young single woman, the daughter of a physician. He had noticed that his daughter, a late teenager, had joined a religious group and declared that she had been 'saved'. Her new life-style of prayer and preoccupation with the scripture confirmed this. But the new life-style was contrary to her own family background and so her parents were baffled and bewildered and could not accept that this was normal behaviour. Indeed they even suggested that it was an illness of a schizophrenic nature. Again, on taking a full history from both parents and daughter, and examining her fully, it became obvious that there was no evidence whatsoever of schizophrenia or any other mental illness. She was a very normal girl who had experienced a sudden clear-cut religious conversion. The parents were reassured and to their merit accepted the fact and allowed her to continue along the way which she had chosen, with her new circle of friends and her new interests.

R. D. Laing, the well-known psychiatrist, gave in his book *The Divided Self* a new viewpoint of schizophrenia. He suggested that the people known as schizophrenics, rather than being ill, were the prophets of the twentieth century with special insights and that later, when we looked back upon this century, this view would be confirmed. However, in my long experience of dealing with schizophrenia it has become evident that this is a severe mental illness which cripples its victims and leads to general deterioration unless appropriate treatment, including drug therapy, is instituted.

When discussions have occurred about the nature of this illness and of the aims of therapy, the schizophrenics themselves in the early stages of their illness, when they have some insight or when they have recovered from an acute phase, always emphasise that what they need when they are actively ill is help through drugs and other means to be rid of their symptoms as soon as possible and for their health and sanity to be restored.

Insanity – Physical (Organic Psychosis)

The last major group of insanities arise from specific physical causes. These may be infections, such as syphilis of the brain which used to be very common and caused general deterioration of the mental processes culminating in general paralysis of the insane. Though this became less common with the advent of penicillin, during the past ten to fifteen years there has been an increase again in the mental and neurological illnesses arising from this kind of infection. It may well be that it is linked with the new morality and the promiscuity of the permissive society where more effective contraceptive measures have allowed an extension of this laissez-faire in the sexual sphere. Another example of a physical cause of insanity is alcoholism which is a poison to the brain and to other organs of the body such as the liver, and can after several years of heavy drinking result in severe deterioration of the brain as well as other conditions which will be described in a sub-section on alcoholism. Mental illness and psychological symptoms can also arise from growths in the brain. The symptoms will be those of insanity as well as physical symptoms specifically arising from the tumour, depending on its site and size.

However, whatever the exact physical lesion, there will be what we term an organic reaction type of mental disorder. There will always occur in a physical insanity the following: disorientation for time, place and person, a lack of grasp of simple general knowledge, a deficiency in attention and concentration and a defective memory either for recent or remote events, or both. As clinicians we know that, if there are defects in these so-called cognitive functions, a physical lesion has to be considered. Usually this is done by taking a careful history and carrying out a thorough examination, including especially the central nervous system. Relevant investigations are then performed to exclude or to confirm the specific physical diagnosis. Such investigations will include blood counts, EEGs, X-rays, isotope scans and CAT scans, which have been proved invaluable in the diagnosis of physical lesions. I must again emphasise how important it is that patients who present with common everyday symptoms, such as anxiety, headaches, chest pains, weakness of arms or legs, difficulty in sleep, loss of weight, or loss of memory, must first and foremost be seen and examined thoroughly by a physician in order to exclude a physical cause. When discussing counselling later, we shall note how important it is that lay counsellors are certain that these kinds of symptom have no physical basis. Every year, patients referred with the label 'neurosis' to psychiatrists, not only by lay people or G.P.s but by other specialists, are found to have physical disease.

When confronted with an organic state one hopes that this will be treatable and transient and often with the symptoms described – confusion and loss of memory – we use the label confusional state. However, if the lesion is progressive and the intellectual deterioration and memory loss continue to grow in severity, then we have to admit that this is a dementing process and the patient is suffering from a dementia, with a specific physical cause. In the elderly, a specific focal cause for this kind of dementing process can rarely be found, but a general overall deterioration in the brain resulting from acceleration of the process of ageing after about the age of sixty or sixty-five is referred to as senile dementia. However, when hardening of the arteries causes this kind of dementia, it is called arteriosclerotic dementia, and there are other groups of dementing processes which occur in middle-age such as Huntington's chorea and Pick's disease and are called pre-senile dementias. Dementias also occur in childhood as a result of infections or metabolic diseases, including the well-known cretinism which results from lack of thyroid.

The treatment of the physical insanities should be the treatment of the underlying physical disease. If the confusion and depression are the result of a lack of thyroid, i.e. hypothyroidism, then recovery can be complete if thyroid hormone is prescribed. If the cause is infection of the brain, then the appropriate antibiotic must be given. If it is a syphilitic lesion, then the appropriate antibiotic for the syphilitic lesion must be given. On the other hand, if there is a tumour which is operable, then this tumour must be removed. Other conditions caused by physical factors, such as alcoholism and drug addictions, will be described in those sections. There is one more intriguing fact that must be mentioned about physical insanities and their diagnosis. At times patients may appear to be suffering from mental illness which results from an organic cause, in that they may be confused and disorientated, lacking in memory, rather slow and retarded, and may in addition have lost weight. However, these symptoms can occur sometimes in severe functional disorders (i.e. without a physical basis) such as endogenous depression, and these features of the illness clear completely with the treatment of the underlying depression. This group of symptoms occurring in functional illness is termed pseudo-dementia and it is so good to be able to reassure people, often middle-aged depressives, who believe that they are dementing when they are depressed, that when their depression is treated their so-called organic confusion and apparent dementia will clear altogether. Nothing is so rewarding as to see patients who thought that their brain had been damaged for ever recover the whole of their intellectual capacity.

4. DAMAGED PERSONALITIES

We have described two major groups of mental disorders, i.e. the neuroses and the psychoses, but there is a remaining third large group which is more difficult to describe, namely the personality disorders. Some authorities bracket these with the neuroses as being deviations from normality, excesses of normal personality traits. They certainly do not warrant the label insanity although some of the more extreme personality disorders, such as occur in the psychopaths with their excessive aggression, at times make them appear mad. The psychopaths are those who are often in the news, having shot policemen or innocent bystanders for no apparent reason except that they have been caught in some antisocial act or who have been involved in a sadistic act towards their wives or children.

These people have exhibited destructive traits in their personality from very early childhood; they are impulsive, aggressive and physically violent; they often take part in antisocial acts. They appear to believe in a strange way that they are immune from being caught and, if caught, from the appropriate punishment. Unfortunately, their behaviour, in spite of punishment, keeps recurring. They do not seem able to learn from their past mistakes and that they will be punished for them. Such a man will in the course of theft severely injure an old woman for a few pounds and then brag about it in the local pub.

Yet these are often intelligent men with good backgrounds, though at times some of them do have low intelligence and come from disturbed backgrounds. It is suggested that the flames of psychopathy die down with age, but it is remarkable how long they will persist. Prisons are full of these people and mental hospitals have their quota, though in recent years there has been a tendency for a change of attitude by psychiatrists and nurses towards accepting into such hospitals people who prove most disruptive.

Church workers and social agencies often get entangled with them. They often have a hard-luck story, plausibly based on sound facts. The tendency is initially to give a great deal of time and energy to help them and in doing so raise their expectations. When they are found to be so destructive, difficult and aggressive, then the helping person wants to retreat. This can be difficult, and is interpreted as rejection by the psychopath. The psychopath remains a big problem for society as a whole and neither medical, legal, nor any other measure has been found successful in dealing with him. Meanwhile, we should continue to try and find some of the basic causes and the best form of management, for they are difficult, destructive personalities.

We use the term personality disorders also to describe those personalities who have neurotic traits which dominate their behaviour. For example, there is the anxious personality whose degree of anxiety affects his whole life-style. There may be the obsessional personality who is so preoccupied with certain ideas of behaviour or acts as to allow them to dominate his life. There are other more severe personality traits that affect behaviour and life-style in a more pronounced way. There is the schizoid personality who is introverted, preoccupied with his own ideas and worries and is unable to make relationships with others, being particularly shy. As a result of this limited capacity to make relationships, he becomes even more withdrawn and sensitive, dislikes criticism and tends at times to become almost paranoid. Often it is this type of personality who develops an overt schizophrenic illness.

Alcoholism

Linked with personality disorders are such other significant groups of patients as alcoholics, drug addicts and sexual deviants. There is a tendency to link them thus because so many of these groups do show disorder of personality, and yet they have very distinctive features of their own. Each constitutes a significant group of disorders that the psychiatrists deal with. *Alcoholism* is regarded as a condition in which the person is dependent on alcohol. This dependency may be psychological and/or physical. Changes occur in the brain with heavy drinking; when the alcohol intake is reduced, withdrawal symptoms occur. There are about three-quarters of a million alcoholics in the United Kingdom. The large numbers at risk can be gauged from the fact that 40 per cent of all age groups are now regarded as heavy drinkers. Men are four times more likely to become alcoholics than women, though the latter are fast catching up, and many are secret drinkers. Recently there has been a marked increase in alcoholism among young adults. Untreated, 30 per cent drink themselves to death, 10 per cent regain some control, 30 per cent continue to have lifelong problems, 11 per cent stop spontaneously.

Increasingly the drinker will imbibe to avoid symptoms of withdrawal; he will give priority to maintaining his alcoholic intake at all costs, sacrificing his social, financial and physical status. He gains in physical tolerance and thus drinks far more than the normal person. He will increase his consumption and extend his drinking over the whole day in order to avoid withdrawal symptoms. He may well be mindful of the fact that a further drink is irrational, yet he takes this further drink. He will start the day with a drink 'to steady his nerves'. He will rush off at lunchtime to the pub to drink with so-called friends or purchase a couple of bottles of wine to drink on his own in the office or at home. Again a call in the pub on the way home, where he arrives to have a cold dinner and increasing hostility from the family, and then more drink 'to drown his sorrows'.

Tragically, as he drinks more, so his friends get less, till when he is over the threshold and a full-blown alcoholic, his friends are no longer around. He has become an embarrassment to them, and his isolation is complete.

His resentment and anger increase with his isolation. Those

nearest and dearest suffer most. The money goes on drink and
there is less and less for food and to pay the bills. He is less
loving, has less concern for his family, and is less capable as a
husband.

His physical powers wane, his libido weakens, yet he begins
to accuse his wife of losing interest in him and he becomes
morbidly jealous.

Physically, he begins to deteriorate – his nausea becomes
more frequent, the tremor of his hands more pronounced and
an embarrassment in public. His performance at work gives
much cause for concern, as he begins to make more frequent
and more important mistakes, till by the time he eventually
goes to his family doctor with vague physical complaints, it is
found that he often has an enlarged liver and disorder of some
other systems of the body.

Alcoholism also kills and breaks up relationships. Families,
which should be sanctuaries of peace and joy, become ghettos
of discord and hell. We so often laughed at the picture given
of the alcoholic and his family earlier in the century, the
boozing father, the neglected children, with the fear of the
tyranny of the evil drink. It is no less a menace today, clothed
as it is in much more sophistication and subtlety. Alcoholism
destroys and kills, it degrades and diminishes persons and
personality.

This applies not only to the obvious drinkers but also to the
secret drinkers at home who revert to their sherry bottles as
antidotes to their boredom, frustration, and the problems of
family life. In addition to angry outbursts and increasing
irritability and disinhibited behaviour, the alcoholic becomes
increasingly depressed, and self-harm often occurs. The
suicide rate of new alcoholics increases eighty times, 16 per
cent committing suicide. The brain shrinks, as proved by
radiology and psychological tests, in about 60 per cent of
cases.

Half of alcoholic addicts have minor hallucinatory experiences on withdrawal and 5 per cent have full-blown D.T.s
(delirium tremens), where there is gross confusion, disorientation, ataxia and considerable agitation and fear, and

15 per cent of patients with D.T.s die from it. Ultimately, the brain may be affected to such a degree as to cause a permanent dementia known as Korsakoff's psychosis, where there is a gross inability to learn a new fact and an impairment of the ability to retain very recent memory, while intelligence is maintained, and often there is confabulation where the patient will fill the gaps with absurdities and lies.

Physical disintegration has already been stressed. In addition to cirrhosis of the liver, there is an increased incidence of respiratory disease, gastritis, peptic ulceration, pancreatitis, vascular disease, as well as of accidents. Alcoholics are also prone to upper digestive tract illnesses and cancer, especially of the larynx. They are very prone to nutritional disorders, especially vitamin B1 deficiency. At first, they become very obese and later there is a great loss of weight. Death ensues 113 per cent oftener than in non-alcoholics of the same age group. Many causative factors are implicated. Social drinking is conducive to some becoming alcoholic. In nations such as France, alcoholism may result from the ready availability in a wine-producing country. Protection against alcoholism, however, occurs in some groups such as the Jews for whom alcohol is identified with religious ritual. Nonconformity in its earlier days preached unequivocally against drink, hence the Band of Hope and temperance societies which were formed specifically to spell out the evils of drink and the need to be teetotallers. Yet, as in the case of total prohibition of drink in the United States, a great number found outlets to have their drink, indeed in large amounts. In some areas of the country which were 'dry' on Sundays, drinking was actually increased. Now it is hardly an issue when leaders in so many spheres are well-known imbibers and the mass, under the influence of the T.V. where hardly a play is performed without the majority of the cast drinking, have come to accept it as the done thing. Supermarkets and chain stores have it in abundance on their shelves, next to the food counters and the children's clothes. It is no wonder that it is a major problem and an increasing one for the country at large and for Christians who must show concern for public behaviour. Even

Christians under stress increasingly turn to alcohol for succour and something to calm their nerves, and when it is so widespread it is difficult not to get caught up more and more in this kind of social behaviour.

Christians may also suddenly get caught up in the management of the alcoholic. Isolated as he usually is, the alcoholic cannot and will not turn to his old, erstwhile friends, yet needs support. The Christian should be understanding and be prepared to give such support to him and his family who may need physical and financial help as well as befriending.

The alcoholic himself will need expert treatment for his physical and psychological state and if he succeeds in giving up his drinking, he will still need a tremendous amount of constant support for a long time. Alcoholics Anonymous give such support and unashamedly they proclaim a religious emphasis in the demands they make upon the alcoholic. The very first step the alcoholic has to take to become a member is to accept that he is no longer able to beat the menace on his own, that he is totally bereft of any strength. He further swears that he will no longer drink and, after such confession, agrees to spread this message to other known acquaintances who are addicted to alcohol. He also agrees that the newfound faith and freedom he has found should be declared to others, who should be sought out and converted to the Alcoholics Anonymous' beliefs, so they also may be saved from this addiction.

Drug Addiction

Two distinct groups are trapped by drugs: there are the young people caught up in the escalating drug culture of the latter half of this century and there is the much larger group of middle-aged respectable people addicted to 'minor' tranquillisers such as Valium and Librium and sometimes barbiturates.

The addicts of the hard drugs, such as heroin, morphia and

its derivatives, cocaine and amphetamines, number a few thousand only in this country, but there has been a considerable increase in the last four years. They constitute a large problem because of the consequences of the addiction and the constant threat to other young people.

The taking of hard drugs spells certain disaster for there is inevitable escalation to more powerful drugs till the victim cannot do without increasing doses. It affects his whole life to the extent that he is prepared to be blackmailed to pay sums beyond his means for more supplies of the drugs and is prepared, under pressure, even to take part in criminal activity in order to gain access to the drug or to the money necessary to purchase it. Physical and mental health suffer and this leads inevitably to a sordid, tragic and lonely death. In the case of L.S.D. (lysergic acid), 'trips' may not only cause great distress but can lead to madness, sometimes irreversible. L.S.D. may not of itself cause madness but it could trigger off such a state in a vulnerable personality.

And the question remains, what about the soft drugs? Leaders of the drug-takers say there is no danger in taking cannabis or smoking marijuana. Hence they suggest that such drug-taking is innocent and accept that it is the done thing among the young in a society where anything goes and where youth believe that they should be free to assert their independence. In such a culture, so-called harmless soft drugs can be passed on, not only the hashish and marijuana but the tranquillising drugs such as Valium and Librium.

In most towns and cities there are satellite groups who are prepared to share the experience 'free of charge' initially, but as the requests for the drugs grow in intensity, so does the demand for payment become more unequivocal and menacing. The drugs themselves, such as cannabis, can do distinct harm, causing lethargy and, more seriously, a softening of the brain with accompanying neurological and psychological symptoms and deterioration in intellectual capacity. In addition, there is ample proof that they lead to the taking of harder drugs, especially with vulnerable personalities, and this leads to further mental deterioration. Wherever soft drugs are passed on, there are 'hard drugs' lurking near by with their pushers exerting subtle pressure which can so easily turn into overt blackmail, with involvement of the addict in criminal activity and conflict with the law.

The Christian church cannot stand aside in the face of this menace and peril to the health of their youth. Christians must understand the dilemma the young face and that it is a question of slavery or freedom and a battle for the bodies and minds of our young. In understanding, we must be able to point out to our children the dangers inherent in drug-taking and be prepared to support them to fight those who would enslave them. We must speak out against the dangers and the actions of people who do pressurise the young in this way, however unpopular that may appear at times. We must, in a positive, loving way, understand and appreciate the need of teenagers and young adults for independence and freedom, but show them a superior way which leads to a healthier and more complete freedom. We must show them that to be filled with Christ's spirit leads to all truth, and that this truth can make us free. To be a slave to Christ is to be free indeed.

The way we help the young addicts applies also to the middle-aged respectable addicts. The minor tranquillisers and the barbiturates are prescribed in their millions in this country every year. The patients can be in danger of becoming addicted, physically and psychologically, and may become confused and disorientated in withdrawal, with a tremendous physical and psychological craving for these drugs. As will be shown later in the chapter on treatments, these are remarkable drugs, excellent therapy for conditions of anxiety and tension. However, they can be abused, as when patients turn to them as a regular nightcap over periods of ten or even twenty years. We older people must, therefore, be careful about condemning the young and should remove the beam of Valium or Librium addiction from our own eye before tackling the specks in the eyes of the young. Who can throw the first stone?

Both groups need to be free and rid of the slavery. Both need the freedom that is in Christ Jesus, our Lord.

Sexual Disorders and Deviations

Sexual deviations and disorders, like addictions, have a basis in personality disorder.

That, however, may not be the complete answer and the facts are much more complicated and varied especially in the case of sexual deviations and disorders. There is a variety of them, ranging from minor to very severe disturbances of personality. Impotence and frigidity are common conditions, occurring usually in individuals who appear quite normal in every other way, and yet producing a tremendous amount of distress which can end in disruption of marriages and divorce.

At the other extreme, severely disturbed personalities such as homosexuals, transsexuals, transvestites, sexual masochists, sadists, paedophiliacs can both suffer great distress and cause it to their victims and their families as well as to other people who come in contact with them.

Sexuality has ever been a problem to the religious man, and the Christian is no exception. The very subject has caused a great deal of concern and worry as witnessed by the fact that so many people are referred to the psychiatrist for help with sexual problems. It is almost a paradox, a surprising one, that in this enlightened age, the age of the permissive society, sexual problems loom so large and that the longest waiting lists in most psychiatric outpatient departments are for the psychosexual clinics.

There is a large part of the Christian church which has found it difficult to accept sex as a wholesome subject; it has been taboo and has remained so to the present day. As a result, generations have grown up surrounded by guilt and inadequacies regarding sexuality. Sex and sin have for long been regarded as synonymous and Nonconformists in particular made a great play of this. The unmarried girl who became pregnant was 'cut out' by the respectable deacon, although he himself might have a wife burdened with her tenth or eleventh child. It is no wonder that, with this kind of attitude in every branch of the Christian church, impotence and frigidity were rife. How can we enjoy sex if it is steeped in a sense of sin?

Therapy begins by gently and graciously encouraging the young Christians, men or women, to accept their sexuality as something lovely and God given. Young men often smile knowingly with relief when we discuss how wonderfully we were made by our Creator. We cannot begin to fathom the mystery of our bodies and can but look in awe at the brain, the heart, the hands, the feet; every system and every organ appropriately and beautifully made. And the genital system – the penis and the vulva – what of them? Were they the afterthought, were they created by some devilish other person? No, no, a thousand times no. The genitalia are part of the whole. We can't live without them. They are an essential part of the whole body. The body, that word used by Paul to describe the church, the bride of Christ.

Beautifully and wonderfully made, and the genital system part of that beauty. The young man should be able to talk with dignity and freedom of his own body. He should talk with freedom of his feelings and his instincts and accept sex as an essential part of the male and female relationship.

A difficult issue for Christians is the question of sex for sex's sake without the procreation of children. And as the brave Dr Jack Dominian, the well-known writer and psychiatrist, has stated, this is a problem of paramount importance. In an over-populated world, with the fashion of only two children to the family and modern means of contraception, sex for pleasure's sake without procreation as an end has become the order of the day. Catholics, who have been particularly concerned with matters of contraception, as well as others, find a dilemma which has been heightened by the recent lead given by the Pope and others, that sex in a mature relationship is God's gift to man.

Sex is the supreme act in a deep, loving relationship, a combination of the union of man and wife before God. Guilt has no place in it, and looked at in this healthy way it can become the beautiful act that God meant it to be. However, when the sacred is sinned against it is the greatest sin of all. 'Lilies that fester smell far worse than weeds.'

Homosexuality is an issue which has been present for

centuries and has been looked at from many different view-points. In the last years it has become even more of an open issue and Christians of all denominations have discussed and tried to give honest answers regarding their attitude towards homosexuality. Psychiatrists have been condemned by homosexuals because they regard it as a sexual deviation or a disorder needing therapy to help the patient to correct his sexual direction. There appear to be two groups of homo-sexuals: those who are lifelong homosexual and not moti-vated to change and those who are arrested in development, with a strong homosexual trait which at times becomes a con-trolling factor. Homosexual activity, by tradition, is looked upon by Christians generally as something to be rejected be-cause of a belief that the Bible unequivocally condemns it. Certain quotations regarding Sodom and Gomorrah are always mentioned in this context, and yet there is a great deal of controversy clouding the issue. It is certain that the vast majority of people, men and women, do pass through a homosexual phase in their childhood and that in a small percentage such traits persist into adulthood. Some of these have led successful lives as married people with children.

However, homosexuality is regarded by many as an illness which they wish to 'conquer' and hence their request to be referred to a psychiatrist. Those who are well motivated to change often do well with psychotherapy and other forms of treatment such as behaviour therapy.

There is little chance of change, however, if the person is not well motivated. One such homosexual, who had been charged with interfering sexually with young boys and was facing a long prison sentence, came for therapy with the sole purpose of remaining out of prison. When this was achieved, he abruptly stopped attending the outpatients' clinic. He was not seen again until faced with the same charge for similar offences, again facing a long jail sentence. He was a powerful advocate on behalf of the rights of the gays and saw no danger in his molesting of young children. However, the writer vehemently disagreed with him and could not condone such behaviour, when young children were involved and liable to be affected adversely.

Homosexuals are often referred to psychiatrists for help for conditions arising from their relationship with their partner. The affair may go sour and there may well be grief or a loss reaction when one leaves the other, or dies, after a long association. Often there is an anxiety or depressive illness and active treatment support is necessary for this.

The Church of England and Nonconformist churches have brought out a number of reports on the subject during the past few years and this subject will continue to be aired in the near future. Whereas compassion must be the order of the day, there is a limit to the tolerance that can be shown and the majority who oppose the development of such activity as marriage of homosexuals in church must give a firm but gentle lead, especially to the young.

Transvestism is another, perhaps more severe, deviation in the sexual sphere. It is the condition where the man usually receives sexual stimulation by dressing up in female clothes. He is liable to be charged (for this is an offence), which makes us wonder why women on a large scale get away with dressing in men's clothes! It is striking that these men often have no trace of homosexuality, appear quite masculine and are often married with children. They receive increasing stimulation by taking risks, sometimes exposing themselves. The condition is rather intractable even after they have been caught in the act. Inevitably this condition, when it comes to light, causes considerable strain on a marriage, which often ends in separation or divorce.

Transsexualism is a condition in which the person wishes to be treated as a member of the opposite sex to the extent of considering having a sex-change operation. Usually the man says that he is a woman inside a male body, that he acts and feels like a female and likes being treated as a female. The opposite, of course, is true of the female transsexualist who demands that she be treated as a man and may consider an operation to be transformed into one. It is remarkable how persistent these people are and therapy does not alter their feelings or motives. However, it appears that when operations have been done to meet their desires, most of them are still dissatisfied. A few became famous by exposure in the media and some, after their sex-change operations, have led quite successful lives.

Sadism with a sexual component and sexual violence seem to be escalating. Sex and violence obtrude upon our lives, particularly in television. The two are often depicted as occurring together. Society, fed on a diet of sex and violence on screen, in newspapers and magazines, inevitably gets caught up with this attitude and the idea often becomes the act. Recently a boy facing a charge of murder gloatingly said to me that he had seen exactly how it was done on the television.

We have shown that there can be different kinds of mental disorder and psychiatric illness, ranging from the mild neurotic conditions to the severe insanities and personality disorders. The first step in management is diagnosis. This is true of medicine as a whole and it is equally true of clinical psychiatry.

B. TREATMENTS

5. AWAKENINGS

Nihilism pervaded psychiatric treatment up to thirty years ago. During the last quarter of a century, however, there has been an explosion of new treatments and innovations in the management of the mentally ill. There has been nothing short of a revolution in the prospect for recovery from these formerly crippling illnesses. To witness the discovery and introduction of these revolutionary treatments in the 1950s made one say with the poet, 'Bliss was it in that dawn to be alive,/But to be young was very heaven'.

Extremely effective drugs were introduced and their effects on psychological symptoms were such as had never been witnessed in the previous thousand years. Two or three individual psychiatrists in different parts of the United Kingdom began at the same time to create a new attitude within their hospitals towards the management of the mentally ill. They began to look upon the patients as men and women who should have greater freedom and responsibility. This new attitude, together with the effectiveness of the new drugs, resulted in patients recovering enough to be discharged from hospitals. This trickle became a flood so that the gates of the Belsen-like Victorian buildings were flung open, and those who had been incarcerated for years emerged into the world outside.

People who had been dumb began to speak, the deaf began to hear and the withdrawn became alive. Wards within these hospitals became therapeutic communities and people began to relate to one another as well as to their nurses and doctors. The 'long ward' was one which as a young physician I used to visit. It was well named: long in structure, the long interview, long-tall slim charge nurse and long, thin schizophrenics. 'How are you today?' I asked the schizophrenic. 'He is well with no complaints,' answered the charge nurse. 'How do you spend the day, Harry?' The charge nurse answered, 'He does this and that,' and continued in great detail. Again I asked the patient, 'How many visitors do you have?' 'His mother,' said the charge nurse, 'visits every other Sunday and brings him his favourite sweets.'

I collected those patients under my care and placed them in one open ward, with open doors and open windows which let in the fresh air. Soon they were given two suits, one for working and one for leisure to allow them to visit the town. They began to meet in groups to talk and share their likes and dislikes, their loves and hates; they began even to share their criticisms of the ward regime. I remember one day one of them coming to me and asking why could he not join the workmen outside who were rebuilding one of the wards. It took him a year to achieve his ambition. *Adventure in Psychiatry* is the title of a book by Dennis Martin, of Claybury Hospital, which aptly describes the revolution which occurred in the 1950s and 1960s.

It was as a result of these developments that the emphasis shifted to community care and community psychiatry. The patient could be seen early in the community, then in the outpatients' clinic of a general hospital, and could be prescribed new treatments, i.e. drugs, electrical therapy and psychotherapeutic support.

When medical and social histories of the latter half of the century are written, historians will undoubtedly see that these developments in the field of mental health were as great as in any other sphere of medicine. The new antipsychotic and antidepressant drugs rivalled the antibiotics in the benefits that they brought to patients. Largactil will rank with penicillin as 'top of the pops' of a drug list of the twentieth century. New personalities for old is as great if not a greater achievement than new hearts and kidneys for old; less spectacular perhaps, but more effective and lasting.

With the shift of the setting to the community, other professions came to play a greater part in the management of patients. Nurses in the mental institutions always did play a crucial part in the custodial care of these patients. Many gave great and loving care for many years to these unfortunate people and I don't believe that we have yet appreciated the great work they did under difficult circumstances when hardly any treatment was available. It always struck me how well informed the nurses were regarding their patients, their histories and their relationships as well as their needs. Following the famous report of Tooth and Brook, that eloquent advocate Enoch Powell confidently predicted the end of these mental hospitals. Run-down there has been, but no mental hospital has yet been completely closed. I believe that, while their structures remain sound and intact, they will stay in use for at least this century, especially when we consider the economic climate in which we work and serve. Dinosaurs of the past they may well be, yet dinosaurs have an awful habit of staying around well past their appropriate time.

In spite of the continued existence of these hospitals and of the ethos associated with them and in spite of the failure to build up alternative systems, the revolution towards community psychiatry has become a fact. The hospital setting itself has changed with the official policy of building psychiatric units in general district hospitals, thus integrating psychiatry with general medicine. This has brought unexpected side-effects. Those patients of 'best' potential, and perhaps of better status, were hived off and the more disturbed with the worse prognosis were admitted into mental hospitals where neglect has led to a string of scandals over the last twenty years.

However, it is equally true that the advocates of a general district hospital psychiatric unit, who initially believed that they could 'consume all their own smoke' and treat all the patients they were responsible for, found that not all patients did well in this setting and were impelled to transfer many to the local mental hospital. In the last ten to fifteen years people have realised that there are positive advantages in the large mental hospitals. Some patients prefer the pace of the hospital to the general district hospital. There are often extensive grounds which can be conducive to the rehabilitation of the patient and the rehabilitation services generally are far better. However, if for these reasons, the mental hospitals remain in being, then it is imperative that they are linked to a general district hospital unit, with both patients and staff shared and medical consultants visiting both places. If possible the nurses should also have a close link and rotate between the two units.

With these developments came another step forward: the institution of catchment areas. This entailed a team being in charge of a specific area within which they would deal with all patients needing treatment, be it inpatient, outpatient or day treatment. This concept came into being long before the publications which first described it in the early 1970s. It has grown naturally from the other developments, but catchment area psychiatry also meant that there was a continuity of care so that a patient treated by one doctor and his team in the community would have the same team if admitted into hospital. This helped a great deal to allay the fears that are so often felt by patients admitted to a psychiatric unit or mental hospital.

The team was an essential element of this concept. The members worked in the same setting dealing with the same patients. Much has been written about this multidisciplinary approach, but in reality what it means is that people with a common cause work together for the benefit of their patients. The team usually consists of the consultant psychiatrist as leader, junior psychiatrists, doctors in training, nurses, occupational therapists, industrial therapists, social workers and psychologists. These work closely with the general practitioner, the primary care doctor who is close to the patients and their families, and usually practises within the catchment area. The general practitioner has direct access to members of the team, sometimes joining them on their case conferences, accompanying the consultant on domiciliary visits and maintaining a close link with the community nurses who have a most crucial role to play.

Recently the psychiatrists have gone out more into the field, establishing regular sessions with general practitioners, seeing their most complicated problems in their own surgeries or having discussions with a group of general practitioners about the various psychiatric and related problems they encounter in the practice. Psychologists were active members of the team but recently have become more autonomous and have taken more responsibility upon themselves in treating patients individually and in having direct referrals from general practitioners. The community nurses have become a very important link between the hospital-based doctors and the general practitioners. They visit the patients at home to assess and mark their progress and help with active treatment such as giving injections of phenothiazine. They also have a special role to play in outpatients' clinics such as the so-called 'modecate clinic' where chronic schizophrenics and others come for regular injections of the appropriate drug and for assessment and support.

With the change of emphasis from hospital to community psychiatry, the outpatients' clinic has become an important setting for the treatment of the majority of patients. Increasingly patients are referred by their family doctors to these outpatient clinics where the majority are diagnosed and then referred back to their doctors or treated as outpatients. In addition, day hospitals have been established for patients needing more intensive outpatient treatment. Patients find their own way to the clinics or they are brought by relatives or friends or, if necessary, by the community nurse or social workers. In this way, they never completely lose touch with their families. Social workers also play a prominent part in the multidiciplinary team, some being hospital-based and others working from Social Service Departments within the community. In the 1950s there used to be an elite corps of mental welfare officers who were highly trained and experienced men and women in the field of mental health: unfortunately social workers today have to become experts in every field and are thus relatively less effective in the special field of mental health. Now it is reassuring to note that the Mental Health

Amendment Bill 1982 clearly states that there should be specially trained social workers in mental health. This means that again there may be a special corps of social workers with special expertise in the management and treatment of the mentally ill.

The Mental Health Act of 1959 was a major step forward in the treatment of the mentally ill and embodied many of the concepts and principles which I have described as the basis of developments in this field since 1950. Contrary to popular belief, this Act does not merely deal with the compulsory detention of patients but with every aspect of care of the mentally ill, such as the provision of hostels, day hospitals, day care and day centres and care of patients' finances. The Act also sets standards for private nursing homes and defines the law regarding misdeeds in their management. In addition, there is a part of the Act dealing with the compulsory detention of patients, which is also the main subject of the present Amendment Bill.

It must be emphasised that over 98 per cent of patients are dealt with quite informally so far as hospital admission is concerned and only a few have to be considered for compulsory admission.

However, in spite of the development of community psychiatry and the belief that it is superior to the old regime, we must not lose sight of the fact that hospitalisation remains a valid necessary step in the treatment of some patients. This needs to be stated because hospitalisation seems to have become a dirty word in some circles with the result that when admission becomes necessary it causes anxiety to patients and their relatives. Hospitalisation should be regarded in some cases as a mere incident, an appropriate incident, in the management of the patient.

Hospitalisation means that the patient is taken away at a crucial time from a hostile, frightening environment to places of security. There he will be fully accepted however bizarre his behaviour. He will become less frightened and less disturbed and by being dealt with by professionally trained people, who also must show loving kindness, he will feel safer and more in control of his symptoms and illness. There may well have been, and there may well be again, a slipping in hospital standards, but from my experience I have come to believe that every patient should be made to feel that he or she is the most important person in the world and yet, throughout, the staff must retain their vital professional detachment. There is no need to defend the latter aspect but it may be helpful to explain it.

When my only son was a baby with a high fever and quite ill, I stood by his bed paralysed and unable to help, unable to make any medical decision. My wife reminded me that I made decisions every day about the health of other people, why should I not now be able to do so for my own son? It was because he was my son that the professional detachment was missing. I was incapable of making a clinical decision because I was emotionally involved.

Emotional involvement must never cloud the toughest decision a clinical psychiatrist has to make: whether a patient who refuses admission into hospital should be compulsorily admitted. As stated, one part of the Mental Health Act 1959 deals specifically with this matter. Sections 25, 26 and 29 have become well known not only to psychiatrists, family doctors and social workers but to many patients and relatives and the public at large. The Government, after much deliberation, have rightly accepted the basic maxim that there is a group, albeit a very small group of people, who will need to be detained compulsorily. Strict criteria have been present since the 1959 Act regarding such admissions. These strict criteria are to be tightened even further as a result of the present Bill. Patients detained in this way must be shown to be suffering from a mental illness within the meaning of the Act, and that they must be a danger to themselves or others and refuse to be admitted informally.

There is no doubt that at times some people get so deranged that they have no insight into their behaviour and are prepared to harm themselves and others, even their loved ones. When that behaviour arises directly from a mental illness it is essential to have a way of helping them over the acute crisis and thus avoiding greater tragedy. No one would misuse these powers if they remembered that they should only be used as a *therapeutic* measure.

We have discussed the settings in which the treatment of the mentally ill takes place, pointing out that a change of orientation has occurred from the hospital to the community, yet hospitalisation remains the only option in some cases. We have mentioned the great awakening that has occurred so very recently in the field of psychological medicine and now I should like to describe, in detail, some of the specific treatments that have contributed to this awakening. The first group is physical treatment and heading the list are the drugs, the new psychopharmacological agents which were mainly introduced in the mid 1950s and played such an important part in bringing about improvement in the treatment and care of the mentally ill. Three main groups of psychiatric drugs exist: antipsychotic drugs, antidepressants and antitension drugs.

Antipsychotic Drugs

At the beginning of the 1950s there was a drug used in hypertension, that is high blood pressure, which was found also to have good effects on the mentally ill, especially in damping down disturbed behaviour in schizophrenia. An article appeared in the *Reader's Digest* giving the news of this discovery. The drug was called reserpine. I remember as a young registrar at University College Hospital, in London, having the article thrown to me across a table in my consulting room by the irate husband of a schizophrenic. He had obviously been burdened for years by the chronic illness of his wife. He had underlined the appropriate sentences describing her symptoms and stated, 'That's what my wife is suffering from,' adding sharply that he had come for the reserpine.

Reserpine's life as an antipsychotic was very short-lived because of its own side-effects, but also because a 'wonder

drug' named Largactil (biochemically termed chlorpromazine) was introduced soon after. Largactil was first used by
anaesthetists as premedication because they knew that it had
sedative effects, but soon we realised that the drug was
extremely effective in damping down the severe symptoms of
schizophrenia, such as delusions, hallucinations and bizarre
disturbed behaviour. I shall never forget the first time it was
used in a ward of very disturbed chronic schizophrenics,
crowded together with their massive delusions and hallucinations. It was quite amazing to see the difference Largactil
made.

Over a period of several years, I witnessed a large controlled trial of this drug, although this was without the sophistication of modern techniques and statistical evaluation. Largactil was prescribed for the male side of the mental hospital
where I worked while the female side was treated conserva-
tively. Symptoms among the male patients which had been
present for years cleared in a short time, delusions and
hallucinations disappeared and behaviour in the wards
changed dramatically. There was less tension, less violence,
less conflict and less madness. The men began to look and act
more like human beings and to overcome not only the symptoms of their illness but the influence of their long stay in a
mental hospital, which we later came to recognise as institu-
tional neurosis.

Largactil and other drugs of the phenothiazine group can
help patients to get rid of psychotic symptoms such as delusions and hallucinations. These drugs control agitation and
disturbed behaviour, whether this is the result of such functional insanities as schizophrenia or insanities arising from
organic conditions. They are the drugs which are chosen for
the control of schizophrenic symptoms both during the acute
phase of the illness and also as maintenance therapy for the
chronic stage. Their efficacy has been proved by the fact that
one of the commonest causes today for the relapse of a
schizophrenic is his failure to take the appropriate phenothiazine.

At times there is a vague unease in some quarters and

especially among Christians about drug-taking in general and antipsychotic medication in particular. The doubt arises because of a belief that drugs are not necessary and that other means, such as psychotherapy, should be sufficient. Other factors have caused suspicion of drug treatment; people fear that in this way control is taken away from them and this fear has been enhanced by reports that Largactil and similar drugs are prescribed in the USSR for dissidents admitted wrongly to mental institutions.

Mental deterioration certainly could take place if Largactil or similar drugs were given to normal people, but given to persons suffering from schizophrenia they are most effective and therapeutic. Many Christian patients and their relatives have sought to discuss the matter with me as they have over other kinds of physical treatment such as E.C.T. My answer to them regarding the prescribing of Largactil or any other phenothiazines or antipsychotic drugs for insanities such as schizophrenia is this: If my beloved only son aged twenty-one, God forbid, developed a schizophrenic illness, I should request my G.P. to refer him to the best psychiatrist I know (no names; I wish all my senior colleagues to remain my friends). While realising that I should not be allowed to dictate the course of treatment, I should expect that he be prescribed Largactil or another appropriate antipsychotic drug. What, therefore, is right for my own son I consider right for all other sons and daughters, brothers and sisters, fathers and mothers, who suffer from schizophrenia and similar insanities. It would be negligence for the drugs to be withheld and tragic if anybody interfered with management to the extent of preventing them being given the drugs that would make them well.

It is remarkable that Largactil has remained pre-eminent among the phenothiazine groups of drugs after over thirty years. Others have been introduced, differing slightly in chemical composition and having somewhat different properties. Largactil, in addition to being a very active antipsychotic drug also has a sedative effect, hence its effectiveness with patients suffering from agitation and restlessness. Some schizophrenics, on the other hand, are lethargic and with-drawn and need stimulation. For these, Largactil would not be the drug of choice, especially when there are other anti-psychotic drugs equally effective in ridding the patient of delusions, hallucinations and psychotic symptoms but with additional stimulant properties. Such a drug is Stelazine (trifluoperazine), which was introduced soon after Largactil and has also remained a widely-used antipsychotic drug.

A similarly constructed phenothiazine, fluphenazine (Modecate), is the most potent by weight. It has the special advantage that it can be modified for depot use in schizo-phrenia. This Modecate preparation can be given as an injection once a week or once a fortnight to maintain the improved state of the schizophrenic. As schizophrenia often becomes a chronic illness, this drug has proved to be invalu-able in maintenance therapy. It obviates the need for oral medicine two to four times a day and ensures that disturbed schizophrenics have in fact received their treatment.

Another group of drugs with a fundamentally different chemical structure are the thioxanthenes. This group includes Depixol (flupenthixol), which can be prepared in injection form and given once every one or two weeks. This drug has the special advantage of antidepressant properties similar to the main antidepressant drugs. If, therefore, there is a sig-nificant depressive component to a schizophrenic illness, it is worth trying either Depixol by injection or flupenthixol orally.

Antipsychotic drugs are also termed 'neuroleptic' and rather misleadingly 'major tranquillisers'. Some do have a marked sedative effect, hence they are aptly termed tranquil-lisers, but their most profound effect is to rid the patient of symptoms of insanity.

A third large group of antipsychotic drugs had, as its forerunner, haloperidol (Serenace). Dr Ashley Robin and myself were among the first, if not the first, to use this drug in the United Kingdom and carried out a controlled experiment with it.

Haloperidol has taken its place as one of the major antipsychotic drugs and is the drug par excellence in the treatment of mania as well as for the rapid control of hyperactive behaviour. An injection of haloperidol has proved to be a great boon in acute psychiatric wards, in accident and emergency departments and wherever psychotic-like behaviour manifests itself. It is widely used also on general wards, and particularly surgical wards when disturbed behaviour occurs post-operatively.

Haloperidol is given orally or by injection in mania until the acute episode has subsided and then it may be used in maintenance therapy. It is also used in schizophrenia and allied states as an antipsychotic drug if, for example, there has been no response to phenothiazines. It is useful to know that it has potent anti-emetic properties.

A fourth group of antipsychotic drugs, derived from haloperidol and the butyrophenones, has a prolonged action and is particularly effective where there are hypochondriacal symptoms of delusional intensity. An example of this group is Orap or pimozide.

All these drugs are powerful psychopharmacological agents and not surprisingly, therefore, they have side-effects. (Indeed, in medicine as a whole, drugs that are most potent have the most severe side-effects.) They can cause dry mouth and blurred vision, which is often transient, and in the medium term can cause skin rashes, photo-sensitivity and the more important Parkinsonian-like symptoms of rigidity and tremor. These latter occur more often in Stelazine and haloperidol therapy but remit on withdrawal of the drug and may also be suppressed by the administration of anti-Parkinsonian (anticholinergic) drugs. Anticholinergic drugs are not given routinely with antipsychotic drugs since only a small percentage of patients are affected in this way.

These side-effects are taken into consideration when considering the use of an antipsychotic drug, but they certainly do not constitute an adequate reason for withholding or withdrawing such a drug when it is clearly indicated by the presence of symptoms of insanity.

Many patients who have recovered by the use of these

drugs cry out that they must not be withheld from them if a relapse occurs. When the controversy over drugs versus psychotherapy in the treatment of schizophrenia raged in the 1960s, many letters appeared in the correspondence of the *Sunday Times* entreating us to remember that the schizophrenic's greatest desire when overwhelmed by delusions, hallucinations and symptoms of madness was to be rid of these symptoms as soon and as completely as possible; and this meant recourse to drug therapy. In the novel *Anna*, the author – a journalist and husband of a schizophrenic – described dramatically the destructive effect of this illness upon his wife and himself. He utters a heartfelt cry for the introduction of drug therapy early rather than late in the course of the illness, proclaiming that a few days of antipsychotic drug treatment can be more effective than months of analytic psychotherapy.

To withhold drugs, therefore, is tantamount to negligence and can cause untold suffering to the patients and their relatives. Only those with a limited knowledge and extremely prejudiced point of view can doubt the efficacy of these drugs and the need to prescribe them at the right time, in the right dosage and in the right way, to those unfortunate enough to suffer from schizophrenia.

The drug is only one step, albeit the first, in the total management of the patient. The therapeutic relationship with the doctor, nurse and members of the psychiatric team that he meets in 'his' clinic is also of paramount importance. The chronic schizophrenic does not call at a clinic with his bottom bared to receive a jab from a heartless unfeeling nurse and then leave like a mindless mad man. He comes as 'one of the boys', as a nurse once described her patients to me, known to each other, known to the nurses and doctors, and he will often be accompanied by the community nurse who also visits him in his home between clinic appearances.

The young acutely-ill schizophrenic or the catatonic excited schizophrenic, on being relieved of his symptoms, wants to talk and make a relationship with his therapist whether it is the doctor or other member of his team. No greater insight into a human being's behaviour has ever been given to me than by talking in depth with a schizophrenic as he journeys into an acute schizophrenic episode. Nothing is so frightening as to hear a description of a personality disintegrating, of a man about to 'lose his mind'.

When recovery takes place, thought is regained and the patient is able to talk rationally about the world around and the people in that world. This schizophrenic also taught me how hostile our world is, for he was very sensitive to the 'rough' ways in which we humans deal with one another, man's inhumanity to man, especially in our intimate relationships. He described his feelings of rejection and isolation when those around him shied away from real involvement and empathy.

The schizophrenic needs not only his Largactil tablets or Modecate injections but he also needs a sympathetic psychotherapeutic relationship with someone to support him in his hours of crisis and doubt when he is acutely ill as well as when he is attempting to rehabilitate himself.

Associations of the relatives of schizophrenics have come into being because they felt the lack of this kind of support. They help to deal with their own fears and inadequacy in facing disintegration of personality of their loved ones. Their existence also reflects the lack of sensitivity on the part of doctors and the caring professions that they have not given sufficient support to schizophrenics and their families. These people need explanations, encouragement, understanding and, above all, acceptance and the reassurance that they are not a race apart.

Antidepressant Drugs

The true antidepressant drugs are also recent discoveries. They were first used in clinical psychiatry in the golden years of psychiatric drug discoveries, again in the mid 1950s. Previous to that we had to prescribe amphetamines for those suffering from depressive illnesses. They were effective but merely as boosters. Patients improved for a short while but then would become more depressed when the effect of the drug wore off, and there were other dangers of long-term treatment.

The true antidepressants, therefore, were a great break-through. They elevated the mood, and after initial build-up, sustained it. The 'twins', Tryptizol and Tofranil, the former a yellow tablet and the latter orange, were found to be very effective in depressive illness and came to be known by patients from all parts of the country and, eventually, the world. Indeed, this was a breakthrough on the scale of the antipsychotic drugs. These two forerunners, Tryptizol and Tofranil, were of a group known as tricyclics, by the nature of their chemical composition.

They effectively removed symptoms of clinical depression such as the depressive mood, the early morning waking, loss of libido, loss of weight and other biological symptoms. It can be stated categorically that if these tricyclic drugs, Tryptizol and Tofranil, are taken regularly and in the right dose for a sufficient length of time (two to three months), then 85 per cent of depressives will recover from that particular episode, improvement showing itself within two weeks.

If Tryptizol or Tofranil are ineffective, other antidepress-ants can be tried. Another tricyclic drug, Prothiaden, has a moderate antidepressant effect and less side-effects. The drug Sinequan is an effective antidepressant with a marked anti-anxiety effect; it has fewer side-effects and is less cardiotoxic than some other antidepressants.

If the tricyclic antidepressants are found to be ineffective, then newer chemically-related antidepressants may be tried. maprotiline (Ludiomil), mianserin (Bolvidon) and nomifensine (Merital) are three such drugs which have been introduced in recent years. Chemically-unrelated drugs known as Trazodone (molipaxin) and Zimeldine, are said to have fewer side-effects and are less cardiotoxic than any of the other drugs.

As implied, the tricyclic drugs do have side-effects and

cause minor disturbance such as dryness of the mouth and muzziness, but these are transient and are usually tolerated. More seriously, the drugs may affect the heart and cause palpitations, tachycardia, and in some cases even damage the heart muscles themselves. It is when there are such symptoms that other groups of drugs such as the tetracyclics or Trazodone are tried.

A completely different group of drugs known as the monoamine oxidase inhibitors were once widely used and appeared to be very effective in the treatment of depressive illness. However, since they produced a hypertensive reaction with certain foods such as cheese and wine, a special diet was needed, but this situation was rather hazardous because people tended not to adhere to the diet. These drugs were therefore largely withdrawn and are now used only in depressive illnesses which do not respond to other drugs and as the drug of choice in atypical anxiety depressives with a great deal of phobia as well as obsessional symptoms.

Another drug used in mood disorders is lithium, which was introduced in the early 1950s, but it went out of vogue mainly because the therapeutic and toxic doses were very close together. In the last ten to fifteen years it has again been used and found to be very effective as prophylaxis for mood insanities, especially for relapses of manic and depressive episodes, and also in acute mania.

The question is often asked, espiecally by those who are reluctant to take drugs, how effective are the antidepressants in the treatment of depressive illnesses? Do they effect a cure? Do they prevent relapse? The answer is that during the last quarter of a century, the great majority of patients have been treated successfully in that after one episode is cleared with antidepressant therapy, there is no recurrence. The patient is not seen again professionally by the psychiatrist and lives a full, contented life.

There is a small percentage who have a recurrence of the depressive illness which may again respond to antidepressant drugs. My aim, as a young physician, was to treat with adequate amounts of drug and then stop them altogether. It was after hard experience over many years that I recognised a group of depressives who needed a maintenance dose of antidepressant. While on the drug they remained well, but when it was discontinued they relapsed. My patients and I learned the hard way. My fellow psychiatrists and I are not pill mad. We prescribe these drugs because they are effective; we only go on prescribing them when they are needed. This concept is well established in medicine. A hyperthyroid patient has to control his disorder with a thyroid hormone for varying periods, sometimes for a very long time. The diabetic has to continue his insulin injections for the rest of his life.

There is much in common between these chronic physical illnesses and chronic depression. We know that biological changes occur in patients with endogenous depression: changes in the metabolism of salt, sodium and potassium – hence it would be appropriate to call this kind of illness a biological depression. When one shares this idea with patients, they find it comforting because it gives them an adequate explanation for the horrible physical symptoms that they suffer. Although I have no X-ray pictures – as I would have in the case of a fractured bone – to show the broken spirits of depressives, they are relieved to know that their symptoms, both psychological and physical, are not merely in the mind. The black, heavy cloud which weighs heavily upon them is a very real experience.

I can share with those who doubt the efficacy of drug therapy in severe depressive illness the fact that I myself had those doubts during one period, so much that I conducted an experiment in which I agreed to treat half a dozen patients suffering from severe endogenous depression with psychotherapy alone, over many months. These were patients who were reluctant to take drugs but needed treatment as outpatients. They agreed to contact me at any hour of the day if they felt that the depression had become overwhelming. Every one of these patients ultimately needed antidepressant drug therapy and/or electrical treatment before they recovered, and each suffered a great deal before they did so.

What if one of them had committed suicide? I now believe when a diagnosis of severe depressive illness of this kind is made, drug therapy must be instituted at once. It is the first line of treatment unless there is some specific contra-indication. Antidepressants can clear the symptoms of depression quickly and allow healing to take place.

We recognise that a small percentage do not respond to antidepressant drugs and other forms of treatment must be considered. Indeed, if drugs cannot be taken or patients are unwilling to take them, electrical treatment would have to be considered.

In emphasising the specific major part that antidepressant drugs have in the management and treatment of depressive illness, I straightaway admit that this is not the only form of treatment. Even when drugs are prescribed as the main line treatment, supportive psychotherapy is also needed, but this is made easier by drug therapy. It also must be borne in mind that if the patient committed suicide as a result of his depressive illness, the question of psychotherapeutic treatment would then be merely academic. The need for quick resolution of symptoms is therefore paramount, and it is here that drug therapy and other physical treatments such as E.C.T. are appropriate.

Together with drug therapy, even in the most severe depressive states, there is a need for a psychotherapeutic relationship to be built up between therapist and patient. This means seeing the patient, talking to him, allowing him to talk, and building up an empathy, however halting and retarded he might be. Within that relationship healing will occur. Some groups criticise psychiatrists for prescribing antidepressants and not giving enough time to 'see' a depressive. It may be a valid criticism sometimes, but it is hardly a fair comment on psychiatrists as a whole.

There is a real dilemma here, for I have read in religious publications criticism of the fact that psychiatrists are so drug orientated. The sorrowful thing is that patients who are being prescribed these drugs feel much more guilty after reading such articles. When I wrote a letter countering this emphasis I received dozens of letters from patients and relatives thanking me for helping to relieve them of the guilt they felt about taking antidepressants and other psychiatric drugs.

But I see no need for such a conflict. The drugs should be prescribed if they are needed and indicated. They should be discontinued as soon as there is no further need for them. Good Christians should accept that drugs are God-given. They are God's creation and doctors and scientists have merely discovered them in God's world, found them of use in helping and healing our fellow men, and thus have no right to desist from using them appropriately. They are merely one part of the healing process. We should offend against the laws of ethics and of God if we were to withhold them when they were needed.

Antitension Drugs

The last group of drugs used extensively in psychiatry and indeed in other branches of medicine are the famous or infamous Valium and Librium, that is the antitension drugs or anxiolytics. These are modern sedatives, also introduced in the late 1950s and increasingly used in the '60s and '70s, so that now they are prescribed by G.P.s more than 50 million times each year. They are effective as antitension, anti-anxiety agents, hence their popularity. Latterly, however, we have realised that they can become drugs of addiction and cause severe symptoms on being discontinued, and there is increased condemnation of their use. It is, however, ironic that the very men who advocated their use initially are now in the forefront of condemning them.

No doubt there has been gross abuse and over-use of these drugs. This is not sufficient reason for discarding them from the doctor's armamentarium. Doctors should apply more strict criteria for their use, but this is not always easy, for a doctor who does not prescribe a substance is often regarded by the patient as a poor doctor even though he may offer him an hour to discuss his problem in depth instead of giving him medication. Once the drug has been commenced it is difficult to stop and the oft-heard phrase 'Carry on taking the tablets' often implies poor doctoring. Yet the patient demands a pill.

Recently, a young married woman with four children was referred to my clinic with an anxiety state. Almost her first words to me were: 'I've come for the happiness pill.' God forbid that we should ever discover the complete happiness pill – the pill taken once a year that would relieve us of all our anxieties. This would be the culmination of our progress as the human race. We are already sozzled with Valium and Librium but then we should really become the modern Lotus-eaters, stifled of all ambition and drive, happy with our lot and no longer prepared to strive, let alone to suffer.

'The happiness pill.' No, we do not have it and I sincerely hope we never shall. But the antitension drugs we do possess can be used effectively to release anxiety and should be prescribed for a short period when the anxiety is at its height and when there is specific cause. The drugs can be very helpful in states of severe, acute anxiety and panic. If they are prescribed, as already stated, they should be discontinued as soon as possible to prevent the production of addiction or dependency. Before condemning Valium too hastily, we must remember that it may help to secure sleep which is necessary in some stressful times, and also intravenously it is one of the most effective modes of treating status epilepticus, a state of recurring epileptic fits. It may also control symptoms in withdrawal syndromes and is effective as premedication before major operations and during minor operative procedures.

The barbiturates are also very effective antitension drugs, but went out of favour because of the danger of addiction. We are now faced with the same dilemma regarding Valium and Librium. The answer may well be that we should keep a balance with much stricter criteria for the use of these drugs, prescribing them only for the short term, thus minimising the dangers of addiction, dependency and withdrawal states. Meanwhile, we must learn as men and women to control our own destinies, to face realities and accept that happiness comes from within and not as a result of the pill called 'happiness'.

6. PHYSICAL TREATMENTS

Other physical treatments also breed controversy. Electrical treatment or E.C.T. has been highlighted by a recent report of the Royal College of Psychiatrists which showed clear deficiencies in the equipment, techniques and supervision of E.C.T., and in the training of those who use it. This was a brave effort on the part of the Royal College to put the psychiatrists' own house in order and rightly not to paper over the cracks. The deficiencies revealed by the wide-ranging review and report arising from the thorough investigatory work of Dr Pippard and his team do not, for a second, detract from the efficiency of E.C.T. in certain mental disorders. Indeed, they only remind us that there are certain conditions for which electrical treatment is the treatment of choice and, if given early, it can save lives. It is a fact that many good, effective persons would be alive today if E.C.T. had been given to them early instead of inefficient treatment which failed to prevent suicide. E.C.T., long before this present report, caused controversy and heated argument. It has been called 'shock treatment' and the term 'shock' itself caused a great deal of anxiety. It is a grim reminder of the torture of bygone days and conjured up fantasies about torture still being used today.

Fear may stem from the fact that only a mere twenty-five years ago E.C.T. was given 'straight', that is without either an anaesthetic or a muscle relaxant. At that time it was the only treatment available for disturbed behaviour and chronic mental illness and thus tended to be over-used. Some relatives felt that E.C.T. might have caused something akin to a dementing process. I am aware of these anxieties and they are fully justified because I myself witnessed the giving of straight E.C.T. in the early part of my career, and realise the trauma and anxiety that it engendered in patients and relatives. The treatment was made much more humane and less traumatic when a short-acting barbiturate was used to make the patient unconscious and, later, when muscle relaxants were introduced to take away most of the effect of the epileptic fit. However, we know that an epileptic fit must take place in order for the treatment to be effective, but this fit is modified by the muscle relaxant to such an extent that the patient has hardly any convulsions. The treatment is given twice a week with an anaesthetist giving the general anaesthetic and muscle relaxant and a psychiatrist operating the E.C.T. machine. An average of four to six treatments, or at the most eight, are given to patients suffering from depressive illness. This course is not usually repeated in less than two or three years.

E.C.T. is the most effective way of cutting short a severe depressive illness. When a person suffering from depressive illness has acute suicidal tendencies, it is the surest way of making certain that he recovers before such an irreversible, tragic event occurs. Latterly, I believe that if psychiatrists have erred it has been by giving E.C.T. too late rather than too early. I know of no permanent damage resulting from modified E.C.T. given in the way I have described.

A woman of eighty-four was seen by me at home late one Friday evening. The social worker and I had gone round in circles trying to find her abode. In the end we realised she lived next door to the university itself. Our irritability at spending so much time trying to find the place so late at night soon disappeared when we were confronted with this dear old lady in the throes of extreme despair and depression. She was obviously a pleasant woman who had lived a clean, Godly life, confirmed by her sister of seventy-five and also her daughters who were present with her. Yet she was severely depressed with tremendous feelings of guilt about past minor misdeeds and obviously felt that suicide was the only way out. It was clear that she should be admitted into hospital immediately and, since she was acutely ill with a risk of suicide, it was felt that drugs might take too long to save her. In addition, there was a suspicion of glaucoma, which is a further contra-indication to antidepressant drugs.

We talked at length to her and her family and she agreed to have electrical treatment. After two such treatments there was a distinct improvement, after four she was very much better and after six treatments she was fully recovered – better, said her daughters, than she had been for several years. The joy of the family was unspeakable. When some of her symptoms recurred two years later, they came as a family asking me to give E.C.T., the miracle treatment, immedi-ately. As a physician, my concern was to relieve the old lady of the dreadful suffering that she obviously was experiencing, and it was a joy to see the treatment working wonders yet again. One swallow doesn't make a summer, but this kind of response to electrical treatment has been repeated hundreds of times over. The great numbers that have been helped during the last quarter of a century make any doubts of its efficacy pale into insignificance. The doubts and fears of people must be allayed by careful selection, effective tech-niques and a full explanation to patients and relatives. They must be warned about side-effects and assured that the confusion which sometimes follows treatment is transient and clears within a few days. Recently, a detailed research study found that electrically-treated patients have a significantly lower mortality rate than those treated with neither E.C.T. nor antidepressants.

Informal patients must understand exactly what is being done and then give their informed consent. There is some concern, and rightly so, about the giving of E.C.T. to patients who refuse such treatment. The patient's rights must be upheld at all costs, yet in an emergency if there is full agreement that E.C.T. would be the treatment of choice and a life-saving measure, then it should be given in spite of the patient's wishes. What would it gain him or her to win the battle of consent and then kill himself because of a depressive illness's not being adequately treated? Assessment of the suicidal risk is extremely difficult and we must know a patient well in order to make it. If decisions regarding clinical matters are taken out of the doctor's hands, they will result in defensive medicine which means that both doctor and patient will suffer in the end. Doctors have long gestation periods, longer than any other profession, and training should prepare them to make these decisions of life and death. We are first and foremost clinicians, that is we apply an academic knowledge in the practical sphere. The fears and inhibitions of patients, relatives and the public must be acknowledged and their questions answered. Equally, *they* must respect the commitment and calling of a doctor. It is in this way that respect, trust and a more effective therapeutic milieu are established.

I do not wish to avoid the subject of psychosurgery because it is difficult and contentious, but because I believe it will soon be discarded altogether as a form of treatment in psychiatry, unless there is a new development showing a specific lesion in the brain causing a specific illness needing surgery. There will be need for informed consent by patient and nearest relatives if this form of treatment is undertaken. If the patient refuses consent, the new Mental Health Act 1983 makes it necessary to seek a second opinion. This second opinion will be a doctor chosen by the new Mental Health Commission which is to be set up. Although this doctor will make the clinical judgment, he will also have to seek consent from two other lay members of the Commission.

The only indications for considering cerebral surgery at present are severe chronic depressive illnesses which have not responded to drugs, E.C.T., intensive psychotherapeutic procedures or social management. Such patients are usually pictures of abject misery with feelings of total despair.

Psychosurgery may also be considered for chronic anxiety states and obsessive compulsive neurotic conditions which have not responded to all other available treatments. The very failure of these treatments increases the despondency experienced by the patient, who feels that life has nothing else to offer him.

The remaining treatments are known as psychological treatments and include the psychotherapies which will be discussed in detail in the next section. They may be called 'The Talking Cures'. Psychotherapy is based on the patient's talking to the doctor and the doctor listening and intervening when he believes that it is pertinent. This is done in a trusting empathetic relationship.

Psychotherapy can range from supportive measures designed to preserve or restore the status quo, to deep insight-producing psychotherapy which deals with fundamental problems in depth and then inevitably changes parts of the personality and life of the patient.

I have emphasised that drugs and physical treatments are not given in isolation but against the background of a psychotherapeutic relationship between doctor and patient. This implies that drug therapy and psychotherapy as well as social manipulation may all play their part in patient management. Psychotherapy, however, whether supportive or insight-producing, is a major form of treatment in its own right and is also the most powerful form of treatment. In the next section I shall describe psychotherapy in detail and show how it is related to pastoral care.

As a result of the effectiveness of the new attitudes and the new treatments, the wards became true therapeutic communities where patients were healed. The next inevitable step was a wish to leave the hospital. Great numbers did so and sought new life outside in the community. There was need for the community to care. The community was very slow in responding.

We needed, and still do, an acceptance on the part of society, not only to allow the necessary resources for hostels, day centres and sheltered accommodation to be built, but equally important for society to be prepared to create an accepting, loving environment for these healed people. Christians and the Christian church should be in the vanguard of such a movement, with the church's emphasis on love of brother and concern for the weak, the needy, the naked, the hungry and the sick.

I am sad to relate that the church fellowships seem to have been lacking in such practical concern for the mentally ill.

Very few churches have formed groups to befriend them and give them practical help. Indeed, such groups seem to have great trouble and resistance to accepting such a role. I hope that Christians reading this part – 'The Hurt Mind' – have learned facts about the mentally ill which make them realise how vast and varied a problem it is and how great the need for support and love. As committed Christians we must act worthily of our calling. Commitment to the Lord of compassion leads inevitably to concern for others, especially the weak. The compassion of Christ must be reflected in his followers; this is the essence of the Gospel. God caring and loving. God so loving the world that He stoops and comes into it, breaking the barrier of time and place, in order to reach out to mortals. That is the meaning of the Incarnation. The church today, if she is anything, is the extension of the Incarnation and as such is the means of continuing Christ's work in the world.

The most damning criticism of the church in any age is that her worship has no apparent effect on her members and that she is irrelevant to the world around. The Christian church in the present day faces a stark choice. She can live on the surface; we can become inward looking and close our doors on the dirty, broken lives around us and keep ourselves clean, as we wither away and die. The church irrelevant. Or we can follow Christ and get involved in the dirt and the suffering of this world, that is the needy, sick and sinful; and then at least we may take root and live, grow and bear fruit. This was Christ's way.

What do we as Christians and the churches want – life or death? If we isolate ourselves, die we surely shall. But if we get immersed in the sorrow and suffering of the world, we may live and grow. We classify men, good and bad, saint and sinner. He stands among us with nail prints in His hands, and as we look at the neurotics, psychotics, psychopaths, addicts, alcoholics and inadequates, we must never forget that He died for them, just as He did for you and me.

II
TALKING CURES

A. PSYCHOTHERAPIES

7. BEHAVIOUR THERAPY

Psychological treatments consist of the psychotherapies and behaviour therapy. The latter is based on the learning theories of Pavlov and more recently Skinner. The behaviourist believes that some mental disorders, such as neurotic conditions and some personality disorders, are the result of mal-learning. They think, therefore, that with relearning, the patient's behaviour can return to normal. They tackle symptoms directly rather than deal with problems in depth as is done by some other psychotherapies. The aim of behaviour therapy is to teach patients to discriminate between irrational and rational behaviour. There are various forms of such treatment.

Systematic desensitisation is a successful method in which the patient is gradually exposed to the most feared situation so that tolerance gradually increases. For example, the patient who is afraid of spiders is gradually exposed to very small spiders, spiders of increasing size, then encouraged to touch them and thus gradually the anxiety provoked by them becomes less and eventually clears. Sometimes response prevention is used and this usually involves the patient's being admitted into hospital so that he can be restrained, if necessary, from carrying out useless repetitive acts which may be part of an obsessional neurosis.

Flooding is a 'kill or cure' method. The patient is exposed to his worst fears immediately. For example, his hands are plunged into faeces or urine, which he fears. Because the anxiety will be at its height before the actual touching of the faeces, it can only come down and the patient will have learned to face the maximum anxiety situation. The behaviourists also use *modelling*, where they show by example that patients need not have any fear. For example, if the patient has a fear of cats the therapist will hold the cat in the patient's presence, stroke it and then gradually introduce it to the patient to stroke and encourage him eventually to hold it.

Behaviour therapy is usually more effective in phobic states where there is a specific fear than in any other condition, though it can also be beneficial in more complex neurotic disturbances. Behaviour therapy has been shown to be of value in social anxiety where patients have difficulty in going out and meeting people. Here the patient is exposed gradually to the anxiety-provoking situation until he eventually is able to go out on his own and then later to meet people.

These principles of behaviour therapy have been used in psychiatric units and even in wards of chronic patients. They are known as token economies where the patient has been rewarded for good behaviour, that is behaviour that is conducive to special improvement with a resultant reduction in symptoms. It has been found difficult to maintain the improvement after the patient has left the token-economy ward and the patient has to be extremely well motivated to succeed. Though behaviour therapy has had a great deal of attention in the last fifteen years, there must still be caution in extending it in the clinical situation because it is based on experimental psychology, is unduly restricted to target symptoms and the claims regarding its efficacy tend to outstrip the evidence. In summary, behaviour therapy is a complex intervention and should not be oversimplified, though it undoubtedly works in relieving symptoms in certain mild neurotic conditions, especially phobic and obsessional states.

Psychotherapy is the most powerful form of treatment in the whole realm of medicine. It means new personalities for old, and is the means to deal with problems in depth unlike drugs and behaviour therapy which only remove the symptoms. It is aptly entitled the talking cure, because the patient talks to the doctor, the doctor primarily listens and talks sparingly to the patient when appropriate. It is difficult to put into words exactly what happens in the psychotherapeutic setting during the hour of contact between doctor and patient. The talking means 'communication' in a special supportive setting.

We have all, as human beings, at some time or another been overwhelmed by a certain feeling or a thought arising from experiencing some trauma such as a loss or a failure. We will be aching 'to get it off our chest', just as an abscess underneath the skin is ready to burst and release its badness. It is in the psychotherapeutic setting that we can release such feeling and thought. The setting is a supportive and non-judgmental one in which the physician is prepared to listen to whatever subject the patient wishes to talk about, however delicate or shocking. He will be accepted; this does not mean that there will be collusion with whatever he has done, but he will be listened to with sympathy and an attempt made to understand him and his plight. There will be sympathy and understanding. In other words an empathetic understanding will be established between doctor and patient and this will be a crucial feature of the relationship. Research has confirmed that the personality of the therapist is of the utmost importance in successful psychotherapeutic outcome. Warmth and understanding are essential ingredients in a successful therapist.

The communication is mainly verbal; the patient talks, but non-verbal methods inevitably come into play. A look or a movement can speak volumes. Non-speaking periods, silence, where one might expect words, even long periods of silence may be eloquent about deep underlying problems. An inability to speak about such problems, i.e. a resistance, is very significant, it points to material that obviously is so emotionally charged that the patient cannot speak about it. These resistances must be worked through, in that they are discussed repeatedly in different ways in order to allow the patient eventually to speak about them.

A patient has often asked me after a few therapeutic sessions: 'What do I tell my husband [or wife as the case may be] that we do in these sessions?' What is psychotherapy? One such client added: 'It is striking that we never have a preconceived agenda, we have no small talk, there is no gossip, no talking about the weather. But I feel I work when I come here and my words are full of meaning and my feelings range over a wide spectrum.'

As in every doctor/patient relationship, a trust is built up and confidentiality is of supreme importance. How could one ever reveal anything, especially of a delicate nature, a secret, if we could not trust the other or, indeed, believe that he might divulge such innermost secrets to someone else. Within the psychotherapeutic setting the patient knows that he is able to be himself, that he can set aside any masks in order to see his problems as they really are, i.e. gain insight and be able to do something to rid himself of them.

The reader may be saying to himself or herself, 'Though I am no doctor or psychologist, I often help my friends in this way.' Some people do have a special gift of listening and empathising with others and even of keeping the 'juicy bits' to themselves. This is a form of psychotherapy between friends and relatives and can be extremely sustaining and helpful. This is a level of psychotherapy that occurs also in self-help groups such as Alcoholics Anonymous. The psychotherapy I am describing takes place in a more formal setting, but can take part on different levels, from supportive to deep insight-producing psychotherapy.

8. SUPPORTIVE PSYCHOTHERAPY

Supportive psychotherapy is given with the aim of maintaining the present situation, or sometimes to restore the status quo. This occurs when persons are passing through acute crises and everything seems to be falling apart, it is a 'holding' exercise. So often they are helped by being told and taught to 'hold fast' for the time being. The crisis passes, the clouds clear and the sun breaks through again, although it is difficult during the crisis to believe that it will ever be the same again. Supportive psychotherapy is helpful in all kinds of mental and emotional illnesses. In an acute anxiety neurosis, Valium may be prescribed as a drug of choice but at the same time it will be necessary for the patient to have regular frequent supportive psychotherapy to allow him or her to share anxieties and problems. The relationship supports and sustains. This is true of any close friendship, it should be even truer of a psychotherapeutic relationship.

The depressive will be prescribed antidepressants as a first line of treatment but may also benefit greatly from supportive psychotherapy during the acute phase of his illness. He is relieved to be able to talk to people in some depth about their feelings, especially those feelings of guilt and even sometimes of suicide. This sustaining relationship is therapeutic and a part of the healing process. It gives an oasis of hope in a desert of despair. Even when the drugs begin to act and symptoms have cleared, this supportive relationship is still crucial.

Supportive psychotherapy can also be helpful in chronic mental conditions. Some neurotic conditions become long-standing or there may be recurrent exacerbations of neurotic symptoms from time to time. Some depressives become chronic in spite of the drug therapy and other physical therapies and they need formal psychotherapeutic support as well as aid from self-help groups.

The chronic schizophrenic is a clear example of the need for supportive psychotherapeutic attachment. He needs to attend an outpatients' clinic regularly for drugs such as Modecate injections, but the clinic becomes something special. The patient usually has a psychotherapeutic attachment to one member of the clinic's staff, be it a nurse or a junior doctor. He often has a feeling of attachment also to the clinic as a whole for there he meets with his buddies and those who understand him and are prepared to pass the time of day with him.

Supportive psychotherapy is an essential ingredient in maintaining his improved condition, together with the antipsychotic medication. This reinforces my previous contention that even those suffering from insanity need to make a deep relationship to help the healing process, to maintain any improvement that drugs and other therapies may achieve. These chronic patients are, after all, persons, and we must treat them as human beings with feelings and ideas of their own. They, as much as all of us, need relationships with other people in order that they may feel that they are alive.

9. DEEP PSYCHOTHERAPY

Deep psychotherapy, known as dynamic psychotherapy, aims to effect change in the person. It helps the man to see himself as he really is, that is to gain insight about himself; his words and acts are interpreted as having meaning aimed at gaining that understanding. This psychotherapy also occurs in a formal setting where the patient is seen for about an hour, but much more frequently than in the case of supportive psychotherapy. He is seen once or twice a week and is encouraged to talk at greater depth about his problems and conflicts and to reveal all that he can about himself, his feelings, his loves and his hates, his resentments and his guilt. There will inevitably be considerable release of feeling, especially during the initial interviews when he is unburdening himself. This kind of release of feeling, known as abreaction, may occur at any time; a spontaneous release of a torrent of feeling when the patient may cry ceaselessly or express strong aggressive feelings. It is like an abscess being released and the pain similarly subsides, symptoms clear and the patient becomes less anxious and able to live more at peace with himself and others.

He will exhibit resistances at times, being unable or unwilling to deal with certain problems that are related to his real difficulties. He will defend these at all costs and allow them to remain buried in his unconscious; he may have to be confronted with the fact that he is doing so and have to be helped to work through these resistances. He will be encouraged to talk repeatedly about them in different ways so that they will surface. His words and behaviour in the sessions can sometimes be interpreted clearly as having certain meanings. Perhaps he is ranting and raving against certain persons in his family or at work, or it may be a reflection and a projection of his own inadequacies. These can be discussed then, in detail, and if the patient accepts this as a correct explanation, he may be less fearful when such persons are met in the future. He will gain understanding, and the realisation that there is no need to have such fears of inferiority and inadequacy towards these figures will lead to his increased confidence and improved behaviour.

Dynamic psychotherapy emerged from the work of physicians. This is not an insignificant fact when we view how psychotherapy developed during the first seventy years of this century and it is as well to be reminded of the fact today when so many other professions seem to believe that they may be more proficient at it than doctors. It is of particular significance when one notices how other professions use psychotherapeutic techniques increasingly in various forms of counselling outside the medical sphere. Freud, the neurologist, and Jung, the physician, were great discoverers. It was Freud who found the power of psychotherapeutic techniques after realising the limitation of hypnosis. He was the founder of the deepest form of dynamic psychotherapy – psychoanalysis.

This psychoanalysis embraced both the theory of the mind and psychotherapeutic treatment methods. Freud's psychoanalytic techniques found specific methods of understanding the unconscious where he believed the conflicts which caused the symptoms lay hidden. These included free association – the patient being encouraged to talk about anything that came into his mind, talk about his ideas and feelings at will; and the interpretation of dreams and exploration of slips in everyday language. Freud also emphasised the importance of the feelings that arose in the patient towards the therapist, the 'transference'. These feelings are mainly attitudes from the past transferred to the therapist. These past feelings are obviously often inappropriate to the present and are thus brought to light and transferred from the unconscious to consciousness. They can thus be discussed and dealt with and changed.

There is what is termed a therapeutic, or a working,

alliance between therapist and patient and this leads to a transference situation which eventually leads to the counter-transference, i.e. the therapist's emotional attitudes towards the patient. No doctor or therapist can meet a patient once or twice a week for many months or years without having some feelings towards the patient; and it is important for doctors to recognise and understand these feelings.

These techniques are used in most of what is termed dynamically orientated psychotherapy, that is in psychother-apy in depth which does not reach the intensity of psychoanalysis but which is the commonest form of deep psychotherapy undertaken by most psychiatrists and other psychotherapists.

Patients who are taken on for psychotherapy must have problems which are basically psychological, that is they must be understandable in psychological terms. The patient him-self must accept that this is so. He must also have adequate strength of personality, or 'ego strength' to be able to cope with tensions arising from his inner conflicts, especially when he is gaining insight into his weaknesses, and also have a need to modify his behaviour and change his attitudes and feelings. Lastly, the patient must be able to form and sustain a psychotherapeutic relationship and this is very much linked with the adequacy of his motivation.

Patients that are usually taken on for deep dynamic psychotherapy are those who suffer from the classical neur-otic conditions, anxiety and phobic states and sometimes obsessional compulsive neuroses and hysterical conditions, as well as some minor personality disorders.

Deep psychotherapy can be brief, covering a period of six months, as Malan has shown, and this can be quite effective. On the other hand, it can be a long term lasting several years. It is a time-consuming form of therapy and appears extrava-gant. This is particularly true of the N.H.S. where the num-bers demanding treatment are so great. As psychotherapy in depth is so time consuming it means that only a few can be taken on at any one time by one psychiatrist. However, it cannot be overemphasised how effective this form of treatment can be. It is the psychiatrist's major form of surgery and as such can cause deeper, more fundamental improvement and healing than any other form of treatment, for it goes to the heart of the matter and deals with the depth conditions which are causing symptoms and suffering.

This is the dilemma that the psychiatrists face today. How to give sufficient time to people to deal with their problems in depth. It ill behoves anyone to criticise them unfairly for not spending enough time with patients; there are too few psychiatrists for too many patients. Certainly there is too little time available to cope with all the demands.

I have personally insisted on a minimum of one session a week to be set aside for depth psychotherapy. Sometimes I have been extravagant enough to find two such sessions over certain periods. Those sitting in judgment, noting that I see only three patients during such a session compared with anything from fifteen to twenty patients at other clinics, might criticise me, but the fact is that deeper therapy is carried out. One meets the person in depth and comes to know him, sustain him and lead him into paths of healing which are lasting.

Group psychotherapy is a form of treatment allowing the use of psychodynamic techniques with the additional resources of group dynamics.

These groups usually consist of about eight to ten members and function as a coherent group with current adult relationships between the members as well as sharing feelings and fantasies with the group and its leader. The group can be healing in allowing interpersonal learning or by allowing free expression of feeling. It can also help an individual to gain insight into his problems and support him during his period of change, instilling hope and giving guidance. Sometimes it can act as a family and help correct malpractices that arose in his original family.

B. BUILDING BRIDGES

10. COMMON IDEAS

It is not difficult to see how my insights gained from depth psychotherapy and clinical psychiatry as a whole have strengthened my clinical faith, just as my Christian faith has ever been a source of strength in my clinical work. This arises on two levels, the conceptual and the practical.

I should like first to show how this is so on the level of ideas. The Christian faith and clinical psychiatry each reinforce the central tenets of the other, and as such there is a summation effect which makes one a better clinician. My Christian faith strengthens and sustains me in my hours of doubt when I suddenly feel: Why sacrifice so much time and energy in trying to help people? It sustains me in the moments of making decisions regarding life and death. There are very lonely moments in a doctor's life and Christ's presence then gives that freedom which is essential in making such critical decisions. Conversely there are several psychotherapeutic ideas which reinforce the basic tenets of my Christian faith.

First, there is a mutual respect for man. Physicians start with the maxim that man is a being of great worth and as such revere him, whether they are healing or saving. This is in spite of his atrocious behaviour, the constant exposure of man's inhumanity to man. The ugliness of his acts makes it difficult to respect him. In the Christian faith, the physician has this fact underlined and it gives him the motive power to go on, sometimes against great odds, the patient's lack of motive and the unconcern of relatives.

The patient who comes for help is nothing less than God's

creation, created in His own image, just a little lower than the angels'. He is the type of being whose very flesh God took upon himself in Jesus Christ. It is this man's world which God himself was prepared to enter, breaking the barriers of time and place. Man is a being of such worth that God in Christ would voluntarily surrender Himself on the Cross for the remission of his sins so that he would be reconciled to God while setting aside God's wrath towards him. In this lofty view of man, the stern ethic of the physician psychiatrist finds a well-grounded raison d'être.

Science has in many ways threatened this viewpoint. Man in the modern world arrogantly believes that he can set God aside, but we have become increasingly aware that we are far from being self-sufficient and all-knowing. Sherrington, the well-known neurophysiologist, who spent a lifetime researching the complex nervous system of man, had to admit that '. . . the human mind stubbornly resists all efforts to take its measure and shrinks for ever from the probe of the mechanistic analyst . . .' Sir Martin Roth, the distinguished first President of the Royal College of Psychiatrists, reiterates this sentiment in different, but none the less eloquent, terms, 'for man is always more than he knows about himself and perhaps will always be'. And Schaeffer, the philosopher theologian, reminds us of the importance of man's being linked with God thus: 'When the Bible says that man is created in the image of God, it gives us a starting point. No humanistic system has provided justification for man to begin with himself.'

This sense of incompleteness, and indeed mystery, is the position reached by science itself by the findings of modern physics. The work of such famous scientists as Maxwell, Planck, Bohr, Einstein, Polkinghorne and others has changed the philosophy of science. I hope that I am not oversimplifying the situation by saying that physicists now believe that particles can go through walls; in the study of sub-atomic particles, the act of observation has become one of participation. The basic datum of science is no longer matter but energy; science has moved from atoms through neutrons to plonks. What next? It certainly looks less likely now that Sir

James Jeans overstated his case when he proclaimed: 'The Universe begins to look more like a great thought than like a great machine.'

From the traditions of medicine and psychiatry, from the historical teachings of the church, and now from the realms of modern science, we find good reason to relate ourselves to our fellow men as being wonderfully made and of supreme value. Man is, moreover, a being as much a product of his value system as of his libidinal forces. He is responsible as well as responsive, the being whose moral and religious drives are as real as his sexual and aggressive urges. Samuel Miller rightly stated: 'Believing is as much an integral part of man as eating and sleeping.' There is little that man, even modern man, with all his supposed sophistication, will not believe; man is simply an inveterate, incurable, inevitable believer. He is also a being who asks questions regarding the meaning and worth of his life, the significance of suffering and death.

Psychiatry and Christian faith remind us of the *unity* of man. Running through the New Testament is a common strand which emphasises the importance of all parts of man – body, mind and spirit – and the need to restore wholeness. Wholeness means healing. In the gospels, Jesus healed the physically sick, he restored the mind of the deranged and he forgave sins. Paul in his epistles stresses the unity of man and the need to be strong in body, sane in mind and spiritually mature. Psychiatry also emphasises the wholeness of man and points out the closeness between the physical and the psychological, the importance of psychological factors in the production of physical disease and how physical factors cause psychological illness and shows clearly that healing means the restoring of all the various components.

The psychiatrist is, in a special sense, the complete physician, in that he takes all factors, including physical, psychological and perhaps spiritual, into account in assessing man and his disease and his needs in treatment. Wholeness is health, states the Christian faith, and this is strictly in accord with a special emphasis of clinical psychiatry.

There is another area of agreement between Christianity

and psychiatry: both affirm the centrality of the person and the supreme importance of interpersonal relationships. I have emphasised the importance of assessing, diagnosing and of treating adequately with drugs and other physical treatments, but the psychotherapies are unique as a general treatment of the person rather than a specific attack on the symptoms or the disease alone. In this way psychotherapy, from supportive to deep dynamic psychotherapy, is a health-enhancing procedure. Healing takes place within the whole person as well as in the whole social organism, which includes the patient, the therapist and the onlookers. It must never be forgotten that there is nearly always a participating onlooker, the third person, who is always important whether he or she be in the consulting room with you, or in the waiting-room next door, or even at home waiting for the sufferer to return.

Psychiatry is insistently aware of the importance of relationships to the growth of a personality to health. Without relationships we merely exist. The majestic God of the Old Testament, replete with awesome powers of divinity, always presents Himself as a personal being who is, who seeks, who finds, and continues to speak with men. This personal God of the Hebrews finally, in the latter days, spoke to man through His Son, revealing Himself in Jesus Christ, thus made supremely personal through His life on earth.

Christian faith and clinical psychiatry both look upon man as having a flaw. The plethora of treatments in my profession is proof of the trouble we take to try to change sick minds. They need changing because they are flawed. Flawed, according to one of the leading psychiatrists of the century, Sir Aubrey Lewis, from birth and before. In criticising the psychoanalysts' views of mental health as a state in which man's potential capacities are fully realised, he retorted that every man had deplorable potentials as well as desirable ones.

The New Testament affirms this truth somewhat differently but succinctly: 'All have sinned and fall short of the glory of God.' Christian faith considers that these deplorable potentials are the inevitable consequences of original sin, a theology much maligned by modern, sophisticated, scientific man.

Any system of psychiatry which totally ignores man's obliga-
tions and aspirations in the moral and spiritual order cannot
but diminish his stature and be incomplete.

Often one hears the argument that Freud was anti-
religious. One accepts that this is a widespread belief which
has cast a shadow over psychiatry, helping to make people
generally believe that therefore psychiatry itself is anti-
religion and anti-Christ, a fact not easy to refute, because of
some of Freud's writing and his Jewish background. While
Freud talked about the unconscious, about repression and
conflicts, about urges and instincts, about relationships and
infantile experiences to present symptoms, he was correct,
insightful and authoritative. When, however, he stepped out
of his own sphere of expertise and knowledge, and applied his
theories in another sphere where he had insufficient knowledge and was not an authority, he talked a great deal of
nonsense.

Roland Dalbiez, the French philosopher, and himself a
profound student of psychoanalysis, has established that
Freud did not prove, nor even seek to prove, that religious
beliefs were illusory, but merely made certain peremptory
and unsupported assertions concerning the incompatibility of
science and religion. Nowhere did he try to prove that religion
is a delusion. Anyway, once we cease to deal with the
immediate evidence and common-sense certainty, the application of the concept of delusion to religion becomes a
matter of great difficulty. All the atheistic psychiatrist can do
is to say that a patient holds a conviction different from his
own; he cannot add that it is false because his philosophy is
different. He certainly cannot describe it as a delusion in the
psychiatric meaning of the term, that is a false belief, impervious to reason bearing in mind the person's cultural background. Perhaps it is the atheistic psychiatrist who is deluded.

Both psychiatrists and Christians proclaim that man can
change and be victorious. Psychiatry uses drugs, physical
treatment therapies and psychotherapy to make man whole.
The Christian faith speaks eloquently of God's becoming
man, stooping to raise him, to claim him as His child, to make

him whole by the precious blood shed on the cross. Both approach man as a rational free being capable of making conscious choice. Both reach out to man in persuasion and in love, both refuse to coerce or manipulate him.

The sinner and seeker is allowed to turn his back on Jesus, the young rich ruler whom Jesus loved did so. The patient has the right to refuse his drugs and his psychotherapy which the psychiatrists offer as a means of healing.

Both psychiatry and Christian faith tackle one of man's greatest burdens, namely guilt. Man is so often guilt ridden. Psychiatry differentiates pathological guilt from theological and normal guilt. Pathological guilt may be a symptom of a true depressive illness and will disappear when that illness clears. There may be some guilt reaction to some misdemeanour of the past, a normal reaction which will fade with time and is not of much consequence. However, there is theological guilt where the person believes that he has sinned against God and deserves punishment. This may be based on fact and nothing will clear it except the acceptance of God's forgiveness through the atoning death of Christ.

Next, and surprisingly perhaps, psychiatry and Christian faith are in accord in their attitude towards sexuality. Psychiatry has wrongly been blamed for advocating too much sexual freedom causing widespread promiscuity and the lax sexual conduct of the age. Psychiatry, while advocating a healthier attitude towards sex and a more open discussion about it, never suggests that total permissiveness will lead to health and happiness.

Indeed, psychiatry teaches that order, discipline and respect for others is the basis for healthy and successful living. That order creates beauty is as true of man as it is of a crystal.

The permissive society has accused Christianity of being rigid, narrow, conservative and reactionary towards sexual matters. The Victorian hypocritical attitude to sex, which pervaded many sections of the church, might well have rightly been accused of being reactionary but in essence the Christian faith of both the Old and New Testaments accepts sex unequivocally as an inherent part of man's behaviour on earth and it regards the sexual act as the heart of the marital relationship. The Bible certainly emphasises that the sexual act should remain exclusive for the marital state and is against pre-marriage intercourse, or intercourse outside of marriage, and we forget at our peril that the Ten Commandments were not Moses' laws but God's laws and they were health preserving and health giving laws. We break them at our peril.

Promiscuity has led to young fifteen- and sixteen-year-olds having lived full lives before they even understand what life is about, and being scarred for life before they are out of their teens and before they reach adulthood. Broken marriages abound, with one in three marriages ending in divorce.

Lastly, the great historic doctrines of the church and the scientific findings of psychiatry come together with a resounding accord in their mutual emphasis on the importance of *love* in the life of man. Love and empathy are at the heart of the advances of my own profession; they are crucial in the relationship with our patients; a loving concern is an essential ingredient in all our dealings with men and women in travail.

This parallels Christ's great commandment that we love one another; For God so loved men and women that he gave his only son that such men and women should not perish but have eternal life. It is Christ's love that constrains us in our Christian living and our relationship with our fellow men. It is the very basis of our outreach in service towards our fellow man and it is this love that allows us, as therapists, be we clergy or doctors, to spend and be spent and be made a tool in the healing process, be it in psychotherapy or pastoral care. Paul Halmos, Professor of Psychology at the University of Wales, Cardiff, poses questions in his book, *The Faith of the Counsellors*. Where do the social workers receive their strength from when they reach the limits of their own resources? How can we go on giving and helping without having recourse to some source beyond ourselves? Though Paul Halmos does not state so specifically, he implies that there is a need for a source outside ourselves. This is my experience and the experience of so many of my colleagues, that our strength alone is not sufficient.

For the Christian therapist, Jesus is the answer. Jesus is the unending spring from which we can draw the waters to strengthen and sustain us. This is the water which will never allow us to thirst, but becomes a spring of water welling up to eternal life (John 4:14). This is the eternal spring from which we must inevitably draw our strength.

But difficulties do arise from the synthesis of the Christian faith and psychiatry. For one thing, people accept that psychotherapy has the power to change lives, but they fear it because they believe that it has an element of coercion. The argument is reinforced when we have to admit that the founder of psychoanalysis saw things in terms of mechanistic deterministic philosophy. This arose (as Dr Ernest Jones, Freud's famous Welsh disciple and biographer, shows) from the teaching of Ernst Van Brucke, during Freud's student days, with his concern for aggressive materialism.

Indeed, it is in response to this deterministic philosophical orientation that the roots of the opposition to Freud arose, and not primarily against his brilliant discoveries. In this opposition, initially shaped by his great contemporaries Jung and Adler, we find a valued part of our legacy in psychiatry.

Adler created the school of individual psychology and emphasised the importance of organ inferiority, and also that 'social consciousness' should be the supreme goal of psychotherapy. He dramatically declared that man runs for the prize ahead and that the creative power of the individual is a third force superimposed on nature and nurtured as dominant in the production of a personality.

Jung and his school of analytic psychology produced their own far reaching ideas of psychopathology, among them his theory of personality structure including the collective unconscious, and introduced the concept of the extrovert and introvert. He above all others has recognised the importance of the religious outlook in mental health. He specifically mentioned that he believed this necessary for total recovery to take place and for wholeness to be restored.

The importance of social and cultural factors in shaping personality was emphasised by the American so-called 'neo-

Freudians', such as Karen Horney and Stack Sullivan. Karen Horney's description of man's dilemma in the twentieth century is particularly pertinent today; she delineates man as pursuing possessions, prestige and power, and when he fails becoming frustrated and anxious.

Carl Rogers became a well-known name in the 1960s when he began the movement, which was to extend rapidly, in which psychotherapy was client-centred and the importance of the here and now emphasised and its problems dealt with. It is of note that Rogers came to psychology via a theological background and was outspoken in advocating an individualistic capacity for growth, when nurtured in a sympathetic supportive environment. He reinforced the view that the most effective therapists were those who preserved the characteristics of correct empathy, non-possessive warmth and genuineness. His methods are based on creating a trusting relationship, verbal communication and an increase of understanding. No depth interpretation or resolution of deeper problems is attempted.

The work of Carl Rogers himself led on to groups which came to be known as encounter groups or sensitivity groups, in which the therapists and members play active self-revealing roles and in addition to verbal communication, touching, movement and acting-out become essential parts. Rogers himself was dissatisfied by the over-ready use of such methods. These movements often attract many people who see themselves not as ill patients but as 'blocked' or 'aberrated' from their true selves and others. Frankness may be pseudo-frankness and, even if honest, does not guarantee the elucidation and the solving of the true deep problems. Moreover, there have been casualties among the emotionally fragile and vulnerable. As these groups have moved away from classic psychotherapeutic methods, greater dangers have ensued and we must be warned against such developments, and especially unscrupulous leaders. In all psychotherapy there must be control and discipline and there must be limits of developments in any field. Perhaps we have now reached such limits.

In describing the major developments in the psycho-therapeutic field following and indeed as reaction to Freud, many names and theories have been mentioned and many more could be, but I shall limit myself to two further names.

Berne in the 'sixties, introduced transactional analysis, a term which has been used widely and has come to be recognised as a method where the therapist explores with a client the 'games' he plays with others and the 'scripts' which he has made for his life. This is based on a view of personality as consisting of parent, adult and child ego states. I particularly like the example that Berne gives of a man reverting to his child ego while he sits outside his bank manager's office.

Viktor Frankl was a famous psychotherapist who survived the Nazi concentration camps during the last war and from his experience there tried to answer the question of who become survivors. He was struck by the fact that physically weak people often survived, while others, apparently stronger, died. He found those who did survive, in spite of the atrocious conditions, had a will to live and attempted to find a meaning for their lives and a purpose to go on living. Frankl instituted his special psychotherapy method which became known as existential logotherapy, in which the therapist seeks to bring relevant spiritual realities to awareness. This method is based on the view that man is searching for a meaning and a purpose in life and such a search sustains him through all crises.

A major danger in the emphasis of the psychotherapies is their focus so much on man himself. Paul C. Vitz, himself a psychologist, in his aptly entitled book, *Psychology as Religion* has described the danger of modern so-called humanistic psychology, placing man on a pedestal and suggesting that any difficulties can be erased by him on his own, and that he can by his own efforts become self-sufficient. Vitz shows how this approach, which he terms 'selfism', can turn into a religion with a priest-therapist taking the place of God in receiving the so-called mature man.

The popular 'growth' books are completely based on this selfism. Fosdick's famous, *On Being a Real Person*, now in its twenty-ninth hard-cover edition, and the even more famous,

The Power of Positive Thinking, by Norman Vincent Peale, still going strong after thirty years, are based on the idea of knowing yourself and all will be well. The overriding message and basis of Peale's popularity is his rationalisation and self-realisation. Its selfist character shines through its chapter headings – 'How to create your own happiness'; 'Expect the best and get it'. These vigorously emphasise faith in self, in man alone, and reduce God to a useful puppet of the individual in his quest, despite the frequent references to scriptural and Christian teaching.

This selfism has always been present but brought to a new high by modern psychological emphasis. The mass media daily exhibit this preoccupation with self – in articles, T.V. programmes and advertisements. The world is totally preoccupied and obsessed with itself. Every pain, pleasure and grief is documented, pondered on and morbidly publicised. Human psychology does have something to answer for, but already there is a chink of light in the gloom, as enthusiasm for selfism is already beginning to wane in some quarters. Disillusionment has crept in as more and more people see that it does not after all lead to the promised land of happiness but creates despair as man realises that he cannot live by his own means and powers alone. In being preoccupied with self and putting self and things on the altar to be worshipped lead man to become idolatrous and pagan. But man, in a new wave of disillusionment, is again beginning to see that he cannot live by bread alone, and I believe that in the next decade increasing numbers will turn their backs on the cult of self and will look for a new lead into a new life. My fear is not the existence of this coming wave of returning prodigals – history teaches us of troughs and tides in the affairs of men – but whether the Father's house, the true faith, will still be there to welcome and celebrate their return.

11. PSYCHOTHERAPY AND PASTORAL CARE

Modern psychological insights can be used to make sure that we in the church are prepared for the homecoming. The church may well find its true, relevant ministry in the modern world by meeting the needs of people in the crisis of their lives, in their 'breakdowns', insanities and addictions, and in their difficulties of coping with modern living.

Broken lives are the concern and the opportunity of the church. Jesus was supreme in this. He introduced His public ministry by proclaiming the word that He had been sent to bring good news to the poor, to heal the broken-hearted, to give sight to the blind and freedom to the downtrodden (Luke 4:18).

The church has always had this as part of its mission too. Preaching the good news of salvation and shepherding the flock have been the two salient parts of the church's ministry.

Shepherding has been termed in the modern world, 'pastoral care'. This term was introduced in the 'thirties in the U.S.A. The caring it refers to has been an essential part of the ministry of the church from its very foundation. Jesus cared; He commanded the disciples to take heed of the multitude when they had suggested that the people should be left to go and fend for themselves. Pertinently and lovingly He commanded John at the cross to take care of His mother. The religion of the Old Testament showed the importance of guiding a whole nation. The ministry of Jesus showed the importance of guiding and serving the individual. His great encounters were those with individuals – the woman at the well, Nicodemus at twilight and Peter after the great betrayal.

Is there not something amiss with our caring? Our pastoral care? I shall use this label, pastoral care, though I find it inadequate as a term to describe in essence this caring for people, which is crucial in our Christian ministry and our Christian living.

Our pastoral caring has been found lacking in the last two decades. People no longer turn to the church and ministers for help with their problems; many don't do so because they have not even heard of the Christian church and the Christian faith. Though this seems hardly believable, the fact makes it even more imperative that we strengthen this part of the church's ministry. It implies that we shall have to go out to the people in their needs.

My contention is confirmed by two young ministers who also showed great concern about the lack of depth contact with their parishioners and others. One said, 'In the increasing complexities of our modern life, difficulties arise in our traditional methods of pastoral care. The all-so-nice visiting, monopolised by gossip and trivial talk, is a pure waste of time. We have failed to break through to the *real fears and tragedies of the souls in our care.*'

The second young minister similarly adds, 'We often use the label "pastoral care" to describe the close relationship of a minister and his people, yet it has become merely a method to encourage attendance at services, or to give some advice under specific circumstances or even, in some people's view, merely to call and speak about the superficialities of life.' And we could add – with the T.V. and hi-fi blazing away.

Pastoral care has become a dealing with the superficialities of life and *not* a breaking through to the real fears and tragedies of the souls in our care. And we do not mean only the major, national crises of life, the sunken ship, the bombing outrage, but the countless everyday fears and tragedies occurring in families of all classes. Human beings are equal in their suffering. Despair is no respecter of persons. The fears about our job, of making ends meet, or of ill-health, or of our children's progress, or even our own destinies. Even the most godless man or woman sometime or another will question himself or herself about these matters. When tragedy strikes, as it often does, suddenly and unexpectedly, then the questions become more pertinent. It is at these times that the

Christian should be ready with his answers and his caring.

The church must be aware of the tragedies around it. It is no use being isolated or cocooned, whether as a small enclave or as a sort of air-raid shelter. As a country we are sitting on a time bomb, perhaps two time bombs. Our unconscious anxieties are greater as a result.

Toxteth is no longer merely a name for a district of Liverpool (a misnomer, by the way); it has become the symbol of rebellion in the 'eighties. A trade union leader has stated that if unemployment reaches a figure of over five million, there will be violence in the streets. But conservative Britain (not political Conservative) wants to bury her head in the sand. Toxteth is a symbol of a deep disease of the suffering and anxieties that have to be faced, with the lack of jobs, lack of dignity and the added stress and strain that this brings to families. Some not only fail to find a job but fail to have a hope of ever finding employment, and their very existence is geared to this hopelessness.

The other time bomb is nuclear warfare. When we realise that enough planes fly overhead to blow up the world and destroy it in a matter of seconds, we cannot but unconsciously feel an overwhelming sense of anxiety. This, therefore, is the matrix of our life. This is the background against which we all move and have our being. It is little wonder that we are anxious people. How tragic it is, therefore, that the Christian church has been found wanting in this most essential ministry of pastoral care. Instead people in their hundreds have been turning to psychiatrists, other doctors and other therapists. This reflects both the great need for the Christian church, and the inadequacy of its ministry.

As a Christian, it saddens me that this is so and that worldly techniques seem to be more effective in dealing with bruised persons. While psychiatry is effective, it cannot take the place of Christian faith and pastoral care.

I have shown how on the conceptual level both have much in common and can strengthen each other. I believe that pastoral care today can be strengthened by taking on board many psychotherapeutic insights and techniques. I realise that some strongly oppose this, believing that in taking on these insights and techniques pastoral care is diluted and that it will become mere humanism with a few tatters of religious clothing, having lost sight of its central emphasis of focusing on God. Such would be a real threat if a minister focused his attention excessively on the problems and the solutions of this world. If the minister's faith and theology are weak and there is an overemphasis of the psychological, there is a danger of its becoming a mere human exercise. But psychotherapy can never take the place of pastoral care. All it can do is to strengthen it and help in its practical application.

The church cannot stand still. A static church is a dead church. The whole Christian movement must go on searching for a true pathway to minister to persons in need in the conditions of today, and do so without compromising her heritage or neglecting the advances of science. Pastoral care can embrace aspects of psychotherapy to produce a type of care which neither neglects man nor ignores God.

On the practical level, in the clinical setting, in our daily living, there is much that can be shared between clinical psychiatry and pastoral care. It is because of this belief that I started teaching a church group psychotherapeutic insights and techniques, to allow them to become counsellors in depth. In describing this development, I shall illustrate some of those insights and techniques that can be of value in pastoral care generally.

We accept that counselling on several levels does often occur in a church setting. Befriending is a legitimate and common way of helping people. An informal meeting at which you listen to people talking about their problems, and perhaps give a word of advice here and there, is often very helpful. Self-help groups work on the same level and can prove valuable for sharing common problems. To know that other people suffer in the same way as yourself helps, and a patient can be given advice by another who has gone through the same experiences.

However, in a large, growing church there are times when people with problems need to be ministered to in depth. They can range from the problems linked with breakdowns, anxiety and depression, to those with feelings of guilt and doubt about their faith.

12. A CHRISTIAN COUNSELLING SERVICE

It was clear that many people in the local church had problems which they wished to talk about in depth to somebody. At the request of the vicar, the Canon Roy Barker, I arranged to train a group of lay members over a period of two years. This was a step of faith, my own professional pride had to be broken, and I had to accept the fact that non-medical men and women could be trained in this way. The group met every fortnight in 'term time' (school term), having three terms a year for the two years. In between terms we had a holiday period when the lay persons were able to catch up with their other commitments. We met alternate weeks and the intervening week the members of the group interviewed their clients. Each had one specific client whose case they discussed in the group. In this way, over a period of two years, the group became conversant in great detail and depth with about a dozen cases, which were chosen carefully in order that the members might have opportunities of sharing a variety of conditions and problems.

In addition, special subjects would be discussed and described, sometimes in the form of lecturettes or questions and answers, sometimes role-play would be used in order for the members of the group to have an opportunity of practising their art and for others to watch, learn and criticise. It was essential at the very beginning to discuss and to teach the importance of history-taking. The members were taught to elicit the history of the client, including the personal history, family history, past medical and psychiatric history, and a description of the onset and history of the present complaints and problems (cf. Appendix A).

The first interview was shown to be most important; it constitutes the first contact with the client. It is also the beginning of a therapeutic relationship. One interview alone may be sufficient help for a person, but usually it is only the first of a number of sessions which are used initially to assess the true condition and state of affairs and allow a provisional formulation of the problem to be made and a plan for the future management of the client.

Very early on, a contract would be established with the client. The contract included a plan of action, the frequency of visits, the length, the place of counselling and its aim. The group agreed that whereas we did not wish the counselling to take place within the church itself, it was advisable to have it near by, in a central and convenient place – the church had other buildings in which was found a suitable room for counselling. Such a room is of the utmost importance. It should be well carpeted, with easy, comfortable chairs for both counsellor and client, facilities for the counsellor to write notes and appropriate lighting.

It is not advisable for clients to be seen at home. The situation there does not allow either confidence or confidentiality when there are children and other members of the family around. A demand to be seen at home may be merely a ruse to gain friendship without the client being prepared to face his real problems. This was shown to be one of the major hazards of counselling within the church, where both counsellor and client were members. Indeed, one of the reasons for the formation of such a group was the fact that we were aware that many people sought to be counselled by different people in different homes at the same time and most, while being befriended, never seemed to progress towards a more mature self-sufficiency.

It was striking that one of the immediate results of setting up the training group was that many such people seemed to fade away. Some were taken on for regular, effective counselling and appreciated this, others confronted for the first time with the fact that their real needs and problems would be met in depth either found that their problems were not so important after all or that they did not wish to change. They obviously had not benefited from the superficial roundabout which they had been on for years, though this may well have met some of the needs, not least loneliness.

Most members of the group at first vehemently opposed the concept of a contract with regular meetings for counselling. The vicar was one of those who felt that it might be difficult to put into practice because he had always had his door open to all comers, twenty-four hours a day, seven days a week. Yet, in the end, the whole group, including the vicar, believed that by the use of the contract they had become much more effective counsellors. The people that they counselled gained appreciably from the regular time spent with them; problems were dealt with in a more thorough and fundamental way.

The counsellors' own lives benefited, for they were able to give more regular time to their own wives and children. This is particularly apposite to vicars, curates and other ministers. We tend to demand a great deal of them, from the point of view of time and energy and attention, while forgetting that they also have responsibilities to their own families. This is the cause of much tension, strife, alienation and separation within the families in ministry; many members of such families have been referred for counselling.

The contract helps the client in other ways. There is a tendency among us as humans when we have initial contact with a person in need to give him a great deal of time and attention. This cannot be kept up. Later the time will be limited and the patient or client begins to feel that he is no longer wanted. Indeed, he may well feel rejected and this feeling made more obvious by the discrepancy between the latter lack of attention and the initial great attention. It is much better to promise less than we believe we are able to give later to avoid the feeling of rejection. Giving regular time for counselling in depth and more frequent interviews, rather than few, long time-consuming energy-sapping interviews, does not mean that we have less concern for the patients and less love for them, as has been suggested. It does mean that the love and the feeling that we have for them is channelled into more effective ways of helping them. I believe that three one-hour interviews over a few days is much more effective than five hours at one stretch.

I fail to see how anyone who is suffering greatly can go on talking about his symptoms for hours on end if such symptoms are causing much suffering. From experience, those who have had such regular counsel and who kept a contract have grown and matured far more than those who have merely had a one-off long discussion about themselves and their problems with a counsellor. Of course there may be exceptions whereby, as I have already admitted, marked improvement can occur after the first interview with a counsellor, but this is the exception rather than the rule and the regular, well-conducted sessions where counsellor and client have set aside time for counselling have been found to be much more effective than the haphazard coming together for a chat whenever it suits a person.

Lecturettes given within the training session included such subjects as suicide and attempted suicide; sexuality and its problems; the classification of emotional disorders; what to do with those who are not appropriate for counselling; the limits of our abilities and powers, that is those that we should not take on; what should be done with these and how to refer them to other more appropriate specialists and agencies. Discussions also included other helping groups, such as the Samaritans and Alcoholics Anonymous.

Another feature of counselling which was dealt with in detail was *the art of listening*. This must be accepting and sympathetic, so that the patient feels that he can talk about delicate and difficult subjects, knowing that the therapist will not be shocked or be forced to criticise. Listening to 'silences' can be particularly difficult, especially initially, when most human beings are geared to talk and silences are unwelcome and often embarrassing and difficult to tolerate.

The kind of material which does get revealed depends on the relationship set up between the client and the therapist. If a mutual trust is established a person will speak freely and unburden himself. The moment that a client will say, 'I am going to tell you something I have never told anyone else,' you know that you have pierced his superficial defences and that the healing process has really begun. If you can go on empathising with him, you will allow him to continue to release those things which burden and shackle him and make him less of a person than he need be; neurotic conflicts, difficulties in interpersonal relationships or guilt feelings about his sexuality.

This trust has another essential ingredient, namely confidentiality. The client must know that everything he says is completely secret and in confidence. It is not a gossip session and never, and again I say never, will anything brought out in the counselling sessions ever be divulged to any other person, except on the written consent of a client. It was first given in confidence and must remain secret. How, therefore, I am often asked, should notes, if any, be kept? Note taking is very helpful in recording basic details, noting progress and as an aide-mémoire. By comparing notes, the therapist can ascertain the degree of progress being made and can summarise areas which should be dealt with later. These notes must be kept under lock and key and no one allowed access to them. It must be pointed out that if any legal case arose in which the client was involved, and if the court deemed it necessary, those notes, as well as the therapist, could be subpoena'd. It is well to bear this in mind when writing them, yet one should never be less than realistic and honest in what one writes for otherwise the notes are of very limited value.

Honesty, together with trust, must be at the heart of the relationship between the therapist and the client. If key issues are not tackled, then little progress is made and both will, in reality, be getting nowhere.

A recent article by a clergyman strongly stated that, in his opinion, counselling was a waste of time and that all the hours he had spent counselling had been in vain. He stated that he never knew anyone who had benefited from his counselling. This may be true of the counselling that he had done, but I disagree vehemently with his views when applied generally. I appreciate that that which lacks control and discipline may be a waste of time, and that is why I believe it is worth setting out the criteria for more effective counselling.

Time is precious and we waste it at our peril. This leads me on to consider how long counselling in depth or psychotherapy should be continued. It may be that initially, an agreement will be made for a limited period of perhaps six months and whatever transpires meanwhile, every effort will be made to discontinue it at the end of that period. Alternatively it may be open-ended – which means that it may continue indefinitely.

Often the client will be seen less frequently as the time goes on until he eventually discontinues the sessions. The method of ending counselling in depth is of extreme importance. The most frequent way is to prepare the client for such an event; there can be an agreement between therapist and client that within a certain number of weeks the counselling will end. Meanwhile, the frequency of the visits becomes less and the discussions get more superficial and deal more particularly with the here and now. At this time the therapist may introduce more extraneous subjects, not specifically dealing with a client's problems. The aim is to reduce feelings of loss or grief following the end of the relationship to a minimum.

Sometimes the end is not so smooth. Final parting after all is 'sweet sorrow'. Some, when they begin to become aware that the end is in sight, become very angry and it is easier for them to leave in anger rather than with appreciation. They may feel angry because they think they owe something to the therapist and cannot repay him adequately. Then again, clients may start being late for certain visits or forget to turn up altogether; this is a sure sign that either the therapist is useless or that they are feeling more independent and want to be discharged. Counsellors, beware of keeping the client on for your own sake rather than for his!

Counselling and psychotherapy, like every other form of treatment, have their side-effects. The client may become 'addicted' to counselling. These people always want to be 'in therapy', that is being counselled by someone and as soon as they have ended one counselling course they try to get somebody else to counsel them, or they try to join another psychotherapeutic group; they never want the counselling to end. Counselling has become a way of life and they are so addicted to it that when it ends they have withdrawal symptoms and feel anxious until they find another counsellor or join another psychotherapeutic group.

These people must be shown why they have this need. The inadequacy that it reflects must be realistically dealt with and an alternative way found for them to receive the support they need. Isolation and the need for friendship may be their problem. This should be faced clearly and arrangements made for these needs to be met.

Within the setting of individual counselling there can be other dangers. The feelings that the client experiences towards the counsellor may be linked with feelings in his earlier life or childhood, known as the transference, and may be 'too hot to handle'. It will reach a stage where a woman client may become obsessed with a male therapist. Then the situation must be faced and if not resolved within that therapist/client relationship, the client must be referred to another counsellor.

There is also a danger of inappropriate feelings occurring within the therapist. He may become too angry with a patient to be effective in dealing with him sympathetically. If this happens and is overwhelming, then he must transfer him to another counsellor after explaining why he feels constrained to do this to the client.

On the other hand, a different but equal threat may arise if the therapist falls in love with the client. If this cannot be set aside or contained the client must be transferred immediately to another therapist.

Counselling and psychotherapy call for honesty and trust, not only between the therapist and the patient, but between them and the patient's family. The therapist must be aware of this position of trust and it must never be betrayed.

At the end of the two years' training at St Mary's church, six of the members completed the two-year course and could be regarded as trained counsellors. This proved a great boon because it meant that people in need within the church could be referred to them for help. As the knowledge of their existence spread, more and more people came for help, including those from other churches. We dealt with members of our own church first and then helped others if it was possible.

During the training period, I personally took overall responsibility and provided supervision. If any problems arose in dealing with clients they could ring me at any time. We also brought problems of special concern to the group sessions when we met regularly. At the end of the two years' training I continued to offer this direct supervision to all these counsellors and they had direct access to me any time they wished to discuss a case. In addition, we met every three months for the express purpose of dealing with any problems of individual clients. We also discussed new referrals and chose a counsellor for them. In addition any subject which any member thought fit to bring up, for example, a subject that might not have been adequately dealt with during the two years' training or a new development in counselling or psychotherapy or any new problems related to the group that arose within the church, was discussed.

They themselves now felt confident to deal with people in much greater depth than ever before and so were able to offer a special form of healing to some people in need. However, we always emphasised that they were only one part of the healing ministry of St Mary's. There were other forms including faith healing services, the laying on of hands, and healing prayer groups. None of these should be regarded as being exclusive or in opposition. It is quite wrong for any church to believe that it has an exclusive way of healing and that other churches who believe in a different form, such as the laying on of hands, should be condemned as useless.

The ministry of healing has been a neglected ministry in the church for too long. It would be ideal if a large church had every form of healing within its own confines so that the needs of all kinds of people could be met. Alternatively, a number of small churches could group together to set up a whole spectrum of healing methods. It would be tragic if somebody in need of counselling in depth was turned away from a church because it offered only the ministry of the laying on of hands. For all these differing methods lead to one goal, the healing of the person, and no person or technique heals: God heals. We are merely instruments in His hands.

But men and women have been given intelligence by our Creator, and also the ability to talk and communicate, to feel and make relationships. We can and must use these in the process of healing. This is what psychotherapy and counselling are about and if we do use the talking cures we must become proficient in their use for the benefit of our clients and patients and for the glory of God Almighty.

These are the psychological principles which form the basis of any training in depth counselling or psychotherapy. Such principles are now taught to clergy in theological colleges, and most believe that this is a great help in their pastoral ministry. But, as I have indicated, pastoral care should not be left to clergymen alone. The laity, and not only because of the unavailability of ministers and shocking decline in their numbers over the last decades in every denomination, should take an active part in pastoral care and counselling.

I am aware that this is not a new emphasis. Nonconformists have always emphasised the New Testament teaching of the priesthood of all believers. My own grandfather, an elder in our local church and a miner, visited every family with a member in our church, which numbered over 600, once a year, every year for forty years. We now have more sophisticated methods and the laity certainly should use any new insights which can make them more effective in helping people through the crisis of their lives and at the same time take the opportunity to share the good news of the Christian gospel with them. People are more apt to change in a crisis than at any other time in their lives.

Increasingly churches should assess their needs and find means to set up such training groups. Professional men within the church community will be found with the know-how and experience to train and to teach. Their initial reluctance must be overcome and shown to arise from professional pride rather than overwork!

I found training these lay counsellors an enriching experience. I was able to teach a group of Christians to become more effective counsellors and they in turn taught me a great deal. They showed me that there were many gifted people within our church communities ready to sacrifice time and energy for the good of others and that they were not only talkers but doers of the word. I was amazed how architects, surveyors, carpenters, electricians could study and apply difficult scientific truths and become true clinicians, counsellors and healers. I was overwhelmed by their patience and discernment and by the loving care that they were prepared and able to show towards difficult and unhelpful people. But why should I have been so surprised? They were Christians. They were people who were prepared to follow and serve the Lord.

Many have sought to know what we did in our St Mary's group during those two years of training. More details will be given in an appendix at the end of the book where the general principles of lay counselling will be described in detail. However, I must emphasise that this is merely one method.

The question remains: how far should members of a Christian church be involved in counselling? Should we all be counsellors? Does it mean that every member of a church should become a trained counsellor? If this is carried to its logical conclusion, then the world would be divided entirely into counsellors and clients.

A great number of people are already doing counselling work within the churches or at their places of work, some in professions such as clergymen, doctors, nurses, social workers and others as volunteer workers and ordinary lay members of the church. There are other special groups that do a great deal of counselling such as marriage guidance counsellors and Samaritans. All these could benefit from courses in basic counselling skills such as I have described and which are also available in such organisations as the Westminster Fellowship, the Care and Counselling Society and COMPASS (the Counselling on Merseyside – Pastoral and Supportive Services).

Many in the churches could benefit from attending such courses for counselling, especially if they do individual counselling or are members of supportive groups where people are helped to deal with their problems. Such resource groups can be of particular benefit to a neighbourhood.

I believe that there will be a vast number of people who will not wish to be trained in this way but will go on giving their support and love to their fellow men. Befriending has always been an essential act of man towards his fellows. Befriending means to start with a person as a friend and then to listen, to comfort, to encourage and to reprimand as the need arises. Such people may not want to be trained, indeed they may only be confused if they are trained, but they have their place. We must all recognise our various callings and respect one another in what we try to do, especially when we try to help others to be more at peace with themselves, their fellow creatures and the world at large.

I have tried to make out a case for the pastoral ministry of the church to embrace the new insights of modern clinical psychiatry and psychotherapy. I have jealously noted how the worlds of advertising and business often use these insights for their own good and profit. Christians must be as wise as the people of the world and use these psychotherapeutic insights. I believe that herein lies the great opportunity of the church today where we can 'break through to the real fears and tragedies of the souls in our care'.

Having made what I hope is a powerful case for bridging the gap between psychotherapy and pastoral care, between Christianity and psychiatry, and having emphasised the power of clinical psychiatry in the treatment of emotional illnesses (and psychotherapy as a force to change personalities and heal) I now readily admit that it still falls short of man's needs. For however successful psychotherapy is, it will not take the place of pastoral care and the Gospel message, for psychotherapy alone cannot make man completely whole.

Freud in his later writings admitted such when he recognised that even after long, deep and so-called successful psychoanalysis his patient remained unhappy and unfulfilled. He saw that his subjects when thrown back on themselves could find no comfort or solace in their apparent self-sufficiency.

Within their own framework, psychotherapy and psychoanalysis have no answer. This underlines the extreme predicament of man, for whom self-awareness and self-realisation are never by themselves enough. The answer can only lie, not within the framework of psychotherapy and psychiatry, but within the wider framework of man's relationship with God, who 'was in Christ reconciling the world to himself'. This will constitute the subject of my third part – 'Wonderful Counsellor'.

III

'WONDERFUL COUNSELLOR'

A. SPIRITUAL RESOURCES

13. SOMETHING MISSING

In the first part of this book I gave an outline of clinical psychiatry today, indicating its real value in a society in which pressures on the individual are greater than ever before and at the same time outlining its limitations. While lamenting the existence of so much suspicion and conflict between Christianity and psychiatry I have endeavoured to build bridges between them.

I have emphasised the power of the talking cures – counselling and psychotherapy – and expressed my concern that counsellors within the church, both clergy and lay, use the insights of modern psychiatry and psychology. While emphasising the effectiveness of modern diagnostic and therapeutic techniques in modern psychiatry, I have also accepted their limitations. I have already indicated that Freud, himself a discoverer of psychoanalysis, accepted that many of his patients at the end of a long and apparently successful analysis remained unfulfilled and unhappy. Psychotherapy even in its deepest form does not deal with man's most fundamental needs, his ultimate predicament, the problems of existence and death. It does not deal with his spiritual aspects, the eternal dimension.

Jung, the other giant pioneer of psychoanalysis, stressed this fact even more clearly. In his *Modern Man in Search of a Soul*, he states that, 'men from all the civilised nations of the earth have at some time or another consulted me . . . It is fair to say that all of them fell ill because they had lost that which all the living religions of the ages had given to their followers.

And none had been truly healed unless they had regained their religious outlook.'

The religious or spiritual factor is the essential missing factor. Man cannot be made completely whole unless the spiritual factor is included. 'What does it profit a man if he gains the whole world and loses his own soul?' said Jesus. David in the shepherd's psalm echoes this sentiment when he claims that, 'He [God] restoreth my soul.'

This remains present man's greatest need. His aggressive arrogance merely reflects his inadequacies and helplessness, his hopeless despair and his lost state. A friend returning from South Africa recently, noting the difference between the joyous behaviour of the black South Africans and the moroseness of the people of the United Kingdom, added these significant words. 'You see, they are Christians and have forgiven their oppressors.'

We cannot rule out God from our lives. It is inevitable that the spiritual factor is brought into consideration because man is not only a physical and psychological being but a spiritual one. For complete healing to take place, therefore, his spiritual needs must be met. Spiritual direction and psychotherapy have distinct features of their own as well as similarities. A Christian acting as a counsellor uses insights of modern psychiatry as well as spiritual resources of the Gospel. While all provide different and complementary perspectives on ourselves, our jobs, our problems and our possibilities, all also provide different avenues in which effective help can be given.

Spiritual resources include prayer, the scriptures and the church, its fellowship and sacraments. Counselling and psychotherapy which embrace the use of spiritual resources may be termed Christian counselling or Christian psychotherapy. I am aware that these terms are unacceptable to some. They would point out that there is good, bad or indifferent counselling, any of which may be done by Christians, and others would go further and say that some of the overtly religious counselling is definitely at the bad end of the spectrum.

The critical question is when and how spiritual resources should be used. Any counselling service within the Christian church would legitimately use spiritual resources. Indeed, people coming for such help would expect it to be so and would be disappointed if spiritual direction was not given and spiritual resources not used. If any person does not wish to receive spiritual help he should seek aid elsewhere and there are counselling services where the Christian emphasis is not included. On the whole this is the method used in the N.H.S. setting and in other settings outside the church, which are in themselves quite viable, valid and valuable. Christian counselling and psychotherapy, however, have an extra dimension in using spiritual resources and giving spiritual direction.

In the second section of this book I described the training of a small group from the local church to be effective counsellors. They learnt new psychological insights and put them into practice. In addition, this group from the beginning used spiritual resources and gave spiritual direction. The members of this group at St Mary's church thus used a combination of psychological and spiritual resources and were in reality Christian psychotherapists in the true sense of the word. The other counselling service COMPASS (Counselling on Merseyside – Pastoral and Supporting Services) with whom I have been intimately connected from its inception, as medical adviser, does not generally practise overt religious counselling, although the service arose directly from the churches themselves and remains closely linked with all sections of the church as a truly ecumenical movement.

Christian psychotherapy, therefore, does not mean merely dealing with spiritual problems such as lack of faith, doubts regarding God's existence, and man's ultimate destiny. While dealing with these unequivocal spiritual problems it can also deal with psychological states such as anxiety, depression and loneliness.

I am not infrequently asked how I as a practising psychiatrist and a Christian use the various methods of psychotherapy and spiritual direction. People are curious to know if one uses spiritual resources in one's daily work within the N.H.S. To be frank, there is hardly time to practise even deep psychotherapy let alone give spiritual direction within the setting of the N.H.S. unless you practise exclusively as a psychotherapist. This greatly concerns a great number of psychiatrists as well as other doctors, as it allows us to be open to the criticism of not allowing enough time to talk to patients. Increasingly psychiatrists, as well as general practitioners, are being criticised, not unfairly, for spending merely a few minutes with each patient and being too ready to prescribe a drug, using the oft-repeated phrase 'keep on taking the tablets', rather than giving time to seeking the deeper causes of the patient's anxiety and depression.

My own method is to safeguard at least one session a week to practise deep psychotherapy whatever the pressures, be they demands from new patients, follow-ups or the training of undergraduates and post-graduates.

Even if there were sufficient time to give to individual patients and to carry out psychotherapy in depth, the critical question remains: does one give spiritual direction and use Christian resources within the N.H.S. setting? Generally one does not, but if such is needed and arises naturally in the course of therapy, then one can and does use them. Spiritual direction is given when needed. The woman who was referred because of her persistent facial pain, for which no physical cause was found, in spite of long, detailed physical investigation, suddenly during a psychotherapeutic session broke down and wept profusely, saying: 'I have not had contact with my only son for ten years and have never seen his children.' She described how about ten years previously they had quarrelled over his wedding and neither she nor her husband had attended it. No amount of psychological treatment would have succeeded in healing her condition completely. She needed spiritual direction, advice to get reconciled with her son before she had peace within herself and before God.

Again, patients knowing my Christian standpoint have asked me to pray with them. I willingly do so. A man faced with a fixed guilt which no amount of psychological and physical treatment could remove, asked me if I would pray with him for forgiveness and relief of his guilt. Together we did this and when it was obvious that he had repented before God, his guilt cleared and his symptom left him. Often my consulting-room has become, quite naturally, a 'house of prayer' when I have witnessed the patient forgetting my presence as a therapist and obviously making peace with his Maker. Jesus promised that where two or three were gathered in His name He would be present. He does come. He does bless and heal.

If this is true at times within the N.H.S. setting, it should always be true within the Christian church. Psychological treatment and spiritual direction combined are the most powerful form of therapy imaginable. The synthesis of the psychological and spiritual forces is most effective in making men whole. The Christian psychotherapist is the complete therapist and his aim is wholeness and complete healing.

Not only does Christian psychotherapy deal with man as a whole, with every part of him – physical, psychological and spiritual – it also deals with man's deepest ultimate problems; the problems of man's very existence, his value in this world and his ultimate destiny.

When do we introduce spiritual direction within counselling and psychotherapy? The patient may introduce the subject on his very first interview, when it is clear that such issues are paramount and spiritual direction is indicated. At the same time we, as Christian psychotherapists, should not necessarily 'preach' to our clients as soon as they enter treatment or therapy, for this might be regarded as manipulative evangelism and be unacceptable to the patient as well as to many other people. We may well have to deal with the psychological difficulties and 'blocks' such as their neurotic traits before they are free to make a decision regarding the Gospel message.

It really is unfair to say 'Jesus saves' and suggest that all problems will be solved and all symptoms healed if they merely accept Jesus as Lord. Many people have been disappointed and suffered greatly as a result of feeling 'let down' by this kind of approach. They may accept Jesus as Lord but find that their neurotic problems do not clear. They then feel more let down and guilty and unworthy of being called Christians. These people need treatment for their neurotic difficulties first, before they are in a position to make a full and healthy commitment.

Should Christians always be referred to Christian psychiatrists? No. What most patients need are competent psychiatrists, and the vast majority of psychiatrists will not only be competent to deal with all kinds of mental disorder but will also do so sympathetically, even though they might not share the patient's religious viewpoint, and might not even have any religious beliefs of their own. However, one must admit that not an insubstantial number of Christian patients have complained at the lack of sympathetic handling by psychiatrists and other doctors. Some have described obvious hostility and even disparaging attitudes. These attitudes and practice are completely indefensible and unacceptable, and such psychiatrists should always, as soon as possible, refer these patients to other, more sympathetic psychiatrists. On the other hand, a very small number of Christians might be deterred from seeing a Christian psychiatrist because of the fear that he or she might be too rigid and moralistic and they might not feel free to verbalise all their disturbed thoughts and describe their disturbed behaviour.

Only one such example have I known in my practice and that was a young man with a sexual problem who later revealed that he had difficulties in admitting all his disturbed behaviour to me. He had suffered for years because of having homosexual fantasies and a doubt regarding his sexual identity, though he was a married man with three children. He had been a Christian for many years and played a leading part in his local church. He was able to feel reassured and to express his concern about his fantasies and difficulties and his confidence was restored. At the conclusion of therapy, he said he was pleased that he had persevered with a Christian psychiatrist!

The Christian psychotherapist's position in such cases is clear; while he does not compromise or collude with the patient's disturbed behaviour, he must be able to accept him as he is. He will listen to the best and worst the patient has to say without showing any sense of superiority, censure or disrespect.

The Christian point of view is not shunned but brought into the discussion and often shown to be an important factor in therapy. If any patient found it impossible to express his feelings freely, then he should be referred to another psychiatrist with whom he would have a better rapport.

The Christian doctor should be able to show greater empathy than any other doctor for he has a wonderful opportunity in his contact with his patients to offer something which is unique – the love of Christ. Christian psychiatrists have the opportunity to commend the Gospel, the most potent way being to show a caring, loving attitude. A deep and active sympathy is the least that can be expected from a follower of Jesus Christ. He should also be moved to more than ordinary effort to help. The fact that a psychiatrist is a Christian is all the more reason for his endeavouring to understand as fully as possible every patient's problems and needs, however difficult, dirty or disturbed. This is a speciality in which the love of Christ is more pertinent and can be more potent than any other speciality. It is needed in greater amount and should be available through a Christian psychiatrist. We should effectively share the love of Christ Himself and we should always do so if we always kept in the forefront of our minds that He died for the psychotic, alcoholic and neurotic, just as He did for us. A Christian doctor and psychiatrist should reflect the love of Christ.

As Christian counsellors and psychotherapists we should always be in a position to use Christian resources, including prayer, scriptures, church fellowship and, above all, Jesus Himself, present with us by the Holy Spirit.

14. PRAYER

The first spiritual resource of the Christian counsellor is prayer. Prayer is something which should be as natural to the Christian as breathing. We have misguided views on prayer. We believe that prayers are sets of perfect words, spoken by priests from established books or by experienced Christians with a gift for extemporary public praying. We could not be further from the truth. This concept has been a great hindrance to young Christians.

Praying means conversing with God. It is a two-way process – speaking to God and listening to Him. We can do so direct, there is no need for any intermediate or intercessor. Christ by His work, His living and dying, has cleared the way for any Christian to approach God directly as Father.

It is not eloquent words that are needed but a genuine desire of the heart to communicate with God. We must set aside time to pray. It is no use expecting our prayer life to be rich if we are not prepared to set aside regular and adequate time to be alone with the Lord. We must be regular in our exercise of prayer in order to become efficient in it.

We can be taught to pray. Jesus, at the direct request of His disciples, taught them to pray – 'Our Father, which art in heaven' (Luke 11). It has become the pattern for prayer and can be followed by the simplest of men.

Jesus, the Son of God Himself, was a man of prayer. He frequently, during His public ministry, retreated to His 'inner chamber' to be alone with God. He found His inner chamber on the mountain top, the open sea, or in the quietness of the garden. The rush of our lives militates against this. We are so busy. God is crowded out. But we must find time to be alone with Him. We cannot be right with the world and with our fellow men unless we are right with God. We need daily to

confess our sins and weaknesses to Him and receive His
forgiveness and be cleansed before we can intercede for
others. We are too prone to intercede on behalf of others, to
take a shopping list to Him, before we have even thanked
Him for all His great blessings, confessed our sins and
accepted His forgiveness.

The Christian therapist must inevitably be a man of prayer,
daily exercising this channel to God. Faced with disease and
disorder, be it physical, psychological or spiritual, he is then
adequately armed. We are permitted to know some of the
specific circumstances under which Jesus entered His 'inner
chamber'. He did so just before choosing His disciples. He
often resorted there before and after days crowded with
labour, teaching and excitement. His forty days of tempta-
tions were preceded by days of prayer. And we think of the
bloody sweat of Gethsemane and how even that place became
an inner chamber of prayer and eventually of peace. Jesus
always emerged from His inner chamber calm, strengthened
and re-endued with heavenly power.

And what it was for Him, the inner chamber has become
again and again to His disciples. A child remarked to Principal Rainy, a famous Scottish theologian and a glowing Christian, that she believed that he went to heaven every night
because he appeared so happy every day. Principal Rainy
revealed his secret when he said, 'Joy is the flag which is flown
from the castle of the heart when the King is in residence.'
And what is true of joy, is true also of peace, love and life. The
Christian therapist must be a man of the inner chamber, a
man of prayer. Christians have this great gift of prayer, while
the world continually seeks something similar through various sources of meditation, transcendental and otherwise.
Many have tried various relaxation techniques in seeking
peace and counteracting stress. It has been one of the growth
industries of the last twenty years, and people of all spheres
are prepared to pay large sums of money to be taught such
techniques in order to try to acquire this peace.

Christians, like the Israelites of old, have tended to turn
away from the living God and worship the idols of other

people, the man-shaped gimmicks which will be here today and gone tomorrow, forgetting that the God of Israel has promised never to leave or forsake us, and that His words will last for ever.

The Christian counsellor as a man of prayer can share his experiences with his clients. He can show them how to pray, and pray with them. Above all, he can convince them that more things are wrought by prayer than this world dreams of.

Francis MacNutt, in his first book *Healing*, describes four kinds of prayer:

a) the prayer for physical healing;
b) the prayer for inner healing of emotional problems and past hurts;
c) the prayer of repentance for personal sins; and
d) the prayer of deliverance (exorcism) for demonic possession.

MacNutt's main method of healing, be it physical, psychological or spiritual, is by means of prayer. He emphasises the need to co-operate with doctors and to use this means that they have to treat symptoms of illnesses, but shows that prayer can be complementary to these methods. At times, when the so-called medical methods have been proved defective, prayer may, and often does, succeed.

Jesus healed the sick who came to Him during His public ministry. We, through prayer, may yet call upon Him to heal today. This we can do when the illnesses are physical or psychological. MacNutt calls the prayer for psychological hurts a prayer for inner healing. Such a prayer, combined with psychological treatments, can be most effective. Often there is a spiritual block which prevents physical or psychological healing. There may be present a hidden sin, an anger towards a person which eats up the client, or a hatred of someone which leads to a paranoia. This must be first dealt with by the prayer of repentance for such sin before the physical and psychological symptoms clear. Jesus significantly did not always demand repentance before He healed during His healing ministry but it is noteworthy that He often said to the one whom He had healed, 'Go ye and sin no more.'

Jesus always demanded and found a great faith in Him from the sick person or in some close relative or friend. All our prayers for healing, be it for physical, mental or spiritual ills, must be based on faith, the faith that Christ still has His ancient power to heal and to make whole.

We have become increasingly aware of the close connection between the three types of illness, physical, psychological and spiritual. For many years we have been mindful of the fact that psychological stress can cause physical symptoms such as skin diseases, stomach ulcers and high blood pressure, the so-called psychosomatic diseases. Recently we have become aware that heart attacks and their timing are a result of emotional crisis in a man's life as much as a result of the level of cholesterol or of the fat in his bloodstream or of his smoking. Similarly, people bowed down by guilt and lack of spiritual faith and lack of hope have found life too much of a struggle and have become depressed and suicidal. Sin does cause disease.

I would not agree with J. Adamson, who contends in her book, *Competent to Counsel* that all mental illnesses are the result of sin and are only healed through spiritual means. As I have shown throughout this book, there are many causes of mental breakdown and many forms of therapy which can be helpful. However, I accept that there are some conditions where the spiritual element is paramount and must be dealt with if healing of body, mind and spirit is to occur. And this does not mean mere adherence to spiritual ritual. Jesus warned us that it is no use a man's bringing his sacrifice to the altar if he has quarrelled with his brother. He suggests that it would be better for such a man to leave the sacrifice at the altar and return to be reconciled with his brother first. Too many of us go through the ritual but are not prepared to deal with the anger, envy and jealousy within our hearts.

One professional man, very successful in his own sphere, was cut down in his early fifties by a severe heart attack. He recovered well physically, all his tests showed him to be normal, but he continued to have symptoms such as pain in the chest and raised blood pressure. He had also continued to be very resentful of the fact that he had been ill and the fact that he had been forced to be out of action for many months. His cry was 'Why has it happened to me?' It was only after praying in a small healing group for forgiveness of his resentment and anger and for help to change his attitude that he began to be more at peace with himself and to accept the situation gracefully. His anger reduced, he became much more at peace and he regained his strength so that he was able to return to full-time work.

Often our prayers for healing over the years have appeared to be a sort of mentioning in dispatches, giving a list of those who are ill, with no strong, positive belief that they may be healed. Only latterly with the reawakening which has occurred within our churches, associated often with the charismatic movement, has the ministry of healing become prominent again. Yet over two-thirds of Christ's public ministry was one of healing.

The meaning of prayer must not be misunderstood. It is not something to be tried when all other therapeutic agents have failed. Prayer is essentially the spiritual part of man coming into communion with God and seeking to know His will. Thus our Lord when faced with the appalling prospect of Calvary prayed, not for the 'twelve legions of angels' (Matt. 26:53), but that God's will might be done (Matt. 26:42).

Both private and public prayer may indeed be extremely effective forms of psychotherapy for the Christian. It is a sincere practice of the presence of God, searching in the presence of a supreme standard who is at the same time a loving and understanding Saviour. It is a very different thing from the non-Christian's claim that prayer is merely 'auto-suggestion'. For this reason, effective prayer arises out of the practice of regular Bible reading, so that the mind is prepared, true needs recognised and the source of divine power fully acknowledged.

A prayer meeting, be it the gathering of church members for prayer or a healing group, or a gathering of members for prayer specific for healing, is a valuable form of group therapy. The doubts, fears, hopes and supplications of the participants are heard in united prayer to the one Father. It should, however, be made clear that prayer is not employed primarily for its psychotherapeutic value. The latter is simply a by-product, albeit a very important one, seemingly ordained by the Creator to be such. It is one of the ways that proves sincere prayer is effective. It is also clear that prayer should not be recommended to the non-Christian as a means of allaying anxiety or distress. The promises of prayer are for those who are in the family of God. But to such a member, God has promised to be 'a rewarder of them that diligently seek him' (Heb. 11:6). To those who are of the family, prayer is the most powerful resource of healing and salvation. The more we wield it the more effective it becomes.

Any believer reading these words, who may be suffering physical, mental or spiritual disorder, need not find eloquent words to pray for healing. All he needs to do is to approach the Lord with a contrite, humble heart and say simply and sincerely, 'Father, heal my body, quieten my mind, forgive my sins, in Jesus's name, Amen.'

15. SCRIPTURE

The second spiritual resource is the word of God or the scriptures, and linked with them are the great doctrines of the Christian faith. As Christian therapists, by His spirit we shall be led into all truth as we search the scriptures and share them with our patients. There is power in God's word as in genuine prayer. Those who seek diligently and honestly in God's word, God rewards by revealing Himself and meeting their every need; all the provision man needs he can find in His word. There is no event in life for which God's word does not provide, whatever the need or situation in which man finds himself. Everything we need to know is in God's word; sufficient to meet anxiety, isolation, loneliness, despair, hopelessness, helplessness, depression, fear and sin.

For the Bible gives help in all circumstances. When we are worried, Jesus commands us not to worry for our heavenly Father who feeds and clothes the birds of the air will surely meet our needs (Matt. 6:26).

When we are weary, He invites us to come to take His yoke and share the burdens with Him, and He promises 'rest to our souls' (Matt. 11:28–31).

When we are anxious and troubled, He reassures us 'Not to let our hearts be troubled, trust in God, trust also in me' (John 14:1).

When tempted, we are reassured that 'the father of compassion, the God of all comfort . . . comforts us in all our troubles (2 Cor. 1:3–4).

When lonely, He promises that He 'will never leave or forsake us' (Heb. 13:5). He states that nothing will separate us from His love (Rom. 8:39).

When we face failure, the Word reminds us that God is able to keep us from falling (Jude 1:24, 25).

When we doubt or are perturbed, Jesus guarantees that 'Everything is possible for him who believes' (Mark 9:23).

When we are discouraged and lose hope, we are reminded that 'If God is for us, who can be against us?' for 'In all things we are more than conquerors through him who loves us' (Rom. 8:31, 37).

One of the marks of the Christian is that the Book becomes alive and speaks to him in every circumstance. The Christian therapist must inevitably be a man of the Word – knowing it, understanding it and daily reading it after careful prayer and preparation, and knowing when to apply various passages and teachings to certain specific problems.

We cannot all be first-class theologians, but we should know our Bible and know the meaning and relevance of the great doctrines of the Word of God, such as: God's coming as man, i.e. the Incarnation; Christ's dying as a substitute for man, sinful man, on the cross, i.e. Atonement; to be made whole in the sight of God by faith in the atoning death of Christ, i.e. justification by faith; to know the doctrines of the Bible regarding man and the doctrine of sin, God, Jesus Christ and the Holy Spirit; not only to know them as academic facts and as doctrines but to apply them in our daily living as truths to be believed and as a power to uplift us. We must understand that the atoning death of Christ means that we should not only understand it but allow the reality of Christ's saving power to penetrate the very centre of our being. Here really is the practical application of the basic Christian message of salvation, the belief that Jesus does liberate us from physical sickness, emotional disease and personal sin. Jesus conceived His mission as the coming of one who would bring healing, liberation and salvation to the whole of man – body, mind and soul. Jesus passed on this message to His disciples and gave them the power and the authority over devils to cure diseases (Luke 9:1–2). This message is not merely doctrine but contains the very power of God, liberating man from his wretched state. The disciples preached as the Master preached about the Kingdom of God and cured those who needed healing (Luke 9:11).

There is no such pitiful figure as a doctor with all the academic knowledge who cannot apply it in a clinical setting, except perhaps the theologian with all the academic knowledge who cannot apply it in the pastoral setting.

Many so-called patients who have been depressed have responded to the appropriate antidepressants to a considerable degree, but found that they never fully recovered because they were obsessed with work and more work and continued to justify themselves by work. When we show a patient that what he needs is not more work but less work, more rest – physically, psychologically and spiritually – he can be told the Gospel remedy of justification by faith, and he need not go on trying to justify himself by works, for he can be justified and put right by faith, not by works; that he can be accepted by the grace of God on account of what Christ has already done for him on the cross.

I remember one person from a very select group of Christians who found it exceedingly difficult to come to a full belief in Christ because she believed that her works were not sufficient to justify herself before God. In particular, she felt that her mother was a remarkable woman, who had high standards, with whom she could not compare. For a number of years she strove in vain to reach those high standards and when she failed, as she often did, she became extremely depressed. She only improved a little with antidepressant drugs, but it was not until she came to understand and apply to her own life the doctrine of justification by faith, to understand that while she would never be able to reach the standards that her mother and she herself sought in her, and that Christ had died for her to bridge this gap that she was able to have peace. It was a joyous day when she came to me and said, 'A week ago I was baptised and can at last accept that Christ died for me to erase my weakness and sin, and that I have been made whole through Him.'

Paul declares it in these eloquent words in Romans (5:1). 'Therefore, he is justified by faith, we have peace of God through our Lord Jesus Christ,' and again, in Ephesians (2:8), he says, 'By grace you are saved, through trusting him. It is not in your own doing. It is God's gift, not a reward for work done.' Indeed Paul warns us in Galatians (5:4) that by endeavouring to make ourselves accepted before God by our own human efforts and rejecting God's appointed way of grace through His work on the cross, we put ourselves outside His grace. 'If you try to be justified by the law you automatically cut yourself off from the power of Christ, you put yourself outside the range of his grace.' (Gal. 5:4). Paul in Galatians first points the way to freedom: 'Christ bought us freedom from the curse of the law by becoming for our sake an accursed thing.' (Gal. 3:13).

It would be an accursed thing for us, the cross, yet it is the cross of Christ that frees us and liberates us. All that needs to be done for us has been done on the cross. And, therefore, we must get the cross before all striving, depressed men and women we counsel. The work of Christ on the cross at once cuts through the never-ending rigmarole of pushing ourselves up the slope of achievement, 'to satisfy God and our conscience'. It stops the need to justify ourselves continually. We did not have to merit acceptance, we don't and never shall, but we are *already* accepted before we begin by God who truly loves us. The Cross alone makes it possible for all, including the depressives, the inadequates and the handicapped to be fully accepted.

We must know the Word, know the doctrine, and it is equally important to know how and when to convey them to the counsellee. Above all, when the counsellee asks the oft-repeated question, 'What must I do?' he must simply be invited to admit the Gospel to the understanding of his heart, accept what has been done for him by God in Christ and receive the Christ who has been given.

16. THE CHURCH

The third spiritual resource of the Christian therapist is the church and its various aspects of worship, sacraments and fellowship. The local congregation is the essential nucleus of the church fellowship. At times this may be swollen by special festivals when the church celebrates on a larger scale. The festivals, held under the leadership of the Rev. David Watson during the last few years, have been an example of such celebration when the emphasis has been on the joy and happiness of Christians gathering together to worship the Lord in various ways. This joy, in turn, attracts others outside the church to enquire what is the secret of this joy and seek to share in it and thus be drawn to know Jesus Christ as Lord and Saviour for themselves.

The local church has a more difficult task to continue to be inspirational in its own setting without an injection of enthusiasm from outside, meeting as they do regularly week by week, Sunday by Sunday, in the same building, seeing the same faces. Yet the local fellowship is the most essential form of group activity of believers. Most Christians belong to a local church where they worship regularly.

The local congregation is in reality comprised of men and women who have been redeemed and have accepted Jesus Christ as Lord and are determined to follow Him as the way, the truth and the life. Such people are thus 'walking in the light'; in the light of knowledge of Jesus Christ as Lord and as such should have fellowship with one another. Such fellowship is essential for all true Christians. Any man may at some time or another seek solitude, but no man is an island and no man can live alone. We all seek fellowship and this is especially true of the Christian who feels happiest in the company of fellow Christians.

Strikingly, the Christian fellowship contains people of all classes and colour, all ages and intellect and all backgrounds. The church is the body of Christ and every member is a part of that body, helping to make up the whole. The church needs every member and every member needs the fellowship.

It is because Paul saw the similarity between the relationship of the hand to the body, and the relationship of the Christian to Christ, that we use the term member to describe someone who is a member of the church. 'Now you are the body of Christ and individually members of it' (1 Cor. 12:27). This means in the first place that it is the relationship with Jesus Christ that makes people members of the body. The one who is in Christ is truly in the church. The one who is not a member of the body of Christ cannot be a member of the church; he may pretend to be a member but he really is a bogus member. The true member is one who was bought with Christ's precious blood, one who has moved from darkness into the light of a kingdom; he is one who has risen from death of sin to sit with Christ in the highest heavens.

And because of this he is a member of His body and of His church for it is inevitable that those in Christ will draw together into congregations.

It is a great privilege to be a member of the spiritual body of the Saviour. It means keeping a unity with the head of the church, Jesus Christ, and it means keeping unity with other members of Christ's body. Since the task of his body is to serve the Lord Jesus and His saving mission, it follows inevitably that Christians should share the concern of the Saviour towards people in their suffering, confusion and tragedies.

No Christian can live alone and apart from the fellowship. The cinder which falls from the fire soon loses its glow and dies. The isolated Christian soon loses his effectiveness and even his faith. There are indeed Christians who have taken umbrage over a trivial matter and kept away from the fellowship and in their isolation they have begun to accuse others of not wanting them and in the end have become frankly paranoid. Such Christians are poor witnesses.

Even within churches where they have no obvious rifts and conflicts, there is often a lack of growth within individual Christians in their interpersonal relationships and within the church as a fellowship. Congregations meet regularly up and down the land. The members often greet one another on Sunday with the words, 'Hello, how are you?' and after a few more pleasant superficial words say, 'Goodbye, see you next Sunday.' The brief encounter does not allow any intimate intercourse and certainly no sharing of feelings or problems, or of sharing the joy in the Lord. Yet the church should be a fellowship which is a truly therapeutic community in which growth occurs within the individual person and in his or her relationship with other members of the fellowship. By this I do not mean its being merely a healing community which accepts people who are handicapped, disturbed or disordered, as a sort of hospital ward. Certainly the Christian church should show more love and empathy towards those in need, such as the sick, than any other group, and as I have already pointed out in this book, the church has often been found wanting in this respect. But here I am thinking of a therapeutic community in a deeper sense: a community based on the free flow of Christian love, providing the kind of atmosphere in which people are free to be themselves and to find healing in the redemptive nature of an accepting love. In this way the love of God can be mediated by the members of His church.

We so often use such words as 'love' and 'love of God', but do we put the concept into practice? Do we really mediate this healing love even among our own membership, let alone to the outside world? I am afraid that we have to admit that the discrepancy between our words and deeds has so often corroded the effectiveness of our witness in the world, yet it is this very love exhibited by the fellowship which is not only a living witness to the world of God's love to us but, as Paul reminds us, 'proves to the world that Christ was the Son of the living God'.

Although Paul and other New Testament writers had not heard of Freud's emphasis on the unconscious, and therefore were not looking for signs of its activity among Christians, the very presence and content of the epistles show clearly that these writers were well aware that the lustful self-centredness of man is not set aside when he consciously becomes a member of the church. We, in the Protestant world, have somehow intimated that as Christ has overcome man's sinful condition – an intelligent, intellectual ascent by us to the proposition is supposed to make us automatically God-centred and not self-centred people, to make us holy and good.

Consequently, our modern church – what's left of it – is filled with many people who look pure, even sound pure, but are inwardly sick of themselves, their weaknesses, their frustrations and the lack of genuineness around them in the church. The crucial question of the church today is this: how much change occurs within its fellowship? How do we experience change which leads inevitably to health and salvation, a change which makes the world outside ask questions about us? Surely it is for the church to taste the new wine of the early church afresh and to prove the effects of the work of grace and saving love within our own society.

The church fellowship must also ask: how far should we share our lives together? Too often churches are merely the centres of conventional religious life and a certain standard of behaviour, based on common Christian morality, rather than being centres of the living spirit of Christian love. As a psychiatrist, one often wonders what Christians do with their hates, jealousies, aggression, anger and sexual feelings? Is it not true that we hide them as 'good' Christians? Or are we able to share them with one another in order to emancipate ourselves of these unacceptable feelings and to achieve health and salvation in the love of God? We must learn honestly to accept one another as we are, and not wait until we achieve a certain standard of superficial goodness before being accepted fully into the fellowship.

We all agree that the love of God is the greatest healing power, but this so-called 'love' is a mere empty word in an irrelevant religious vocabulary unless it is experienced and expressed within the fellowship of the church both in word and deed. A new style of life within the fellowship will begin only with a new kind of honesty, an honesty which starts at the point where all really believe that all have sinned and fallen short of the glory of God. Our only hope is to acknowledge our unworthiness, our selfishness and egocentricities and come before the Lord as children in need, honestly confessing our weaknesses and perplexities and accepting His strength and leadership. It is thus that we can start living together a more abundant life, the life of freedom that the Lord brought for all who came to Him.

17. HOUSEHOLDS OF FAITH

Our local church of St Mary's, Upton, the Wirral, had grown considerably during the past twenty years and a large extension to the main body of the church was completed. The vicar, the Canon Roy Barker, was burdened by the thought that in spite of this growth there was insufficient opportunity for members themselves to grow and to get to know one another. The growth itself brought problems in that it was more difficult for people to make relationships with one another in depth and to help one another to mature in the faith.

He had the vision of setting up small groups throughout the parish and of all members who attended St Mary's. He invited two others, an architect and myself, to become with him a trio of leadership, and after careful preparation over many months a plan was drawn to set up 'households'. After a series of meetings with the whole church, the vast majority of the families being represented, it was agreed to invite the members to join the groups and make a commitment to attend them regularly for two years. Forms were sent out to about 450 members and 420 forms were returned, 300 signing a pledge to be members of the households for the specified period of two years and 120 stating that they did not wish to join.

These groups became known as 'the households of faith', a term used by Paul himself in Galatians. Twenty-seven groups were set up, each numbering between six and eighteen, with an average of ten. It was arranged for them to meet once every month, the second Wednesday. This had particular significance because Wednesday was the church meeting-point, that is, the informal midweek meeting of the whole church. Thus the one day when the whole church used to meet was given up to the households of faith, which met in various houses around the parish and beyond. This emphasised the link that the households of faith had with the church of St Mary's.

Everything that happened within the households was also of significance to the church. The groups themselves each had a convener/leader, chosen initially by the trio of leadership. The leaders of the groups met the trio of leadership every two or three months. Most times the groups were divided into three, those who came from the parish met the vicar, those on the periphery met David Bushby, and the groups farther afield met myself. At times all the leaders met the trio of leadership together. The convener/leader often had a deputy and he or she also met the trio of leadership in the absence of the leader. The trio then met together to discuss the results of the meetings of the conveners and to take their advice to modify the households according to what they had learnt from information.

The commitment to one specific household meant that no members could switch to another group at their own whim; they remained members of the same group for two years. There was no escape and each had to confront the others regularly. However, there was considerable flexibility within the groups themselves about the frequency and content of meetings, though they did meet for a minimum of once every month.

Some households met at other times for specific meetings to deal with special subjects; at other times they met socially, and during holiday times they would make special arrangements to meet, for example, during Christmas time.

The usual monthly household meetings might take place in the same house regularly; other groups might meet at different houses at different times. Each meeting had a central theme: Bible study or a tape dealing with such a subject as worship, followed by discussion. They usually met from 7.45 to about 9.30 p.m. and there was always a time set aside for prayer, usually at the beginning or the end of this period. Again, usually during the first quarter of an hour or at the end of the meeting, there would be time for refreshments and socialising.

Of the twenty-seven households, only one went out of existence by the end of the two years and even this household was regrouped for a second term of two years, which meant that all twenty-seven households had been in existence for four years. Some members have moved away from the area and thus left the households, but new members who have come into the parish and become members of the church have joined the groups, each new member signing a form of contract to remain in the group for the appropriate two-year period. Every group allows visitors on up to three occasions, then these visitors have to decide whether to become permanent members of the group or not. At other times households meet on a social occasion and any husbands and wives of members, who do not usually attend, join them, as well as their children.

The rate of integration and progress of the households and the growth of their spiritual lives and relationships have varied a great deal. A few have remained on a superficial level, some have socialised well but have never got to grips with any depth problems and never really made deep relationships with one another. Other groups, however, were far freer and the members were able to ventilate their true feelings towards one another and struggled to make their relationships flourish and these households grew and the members matured greatly.

These latter groups are regarded as the successful ones, true growth cells, where real knowledge of one another led to a loving concern and this resulted in growth and healing. The true purpose of relating to persons on a deep 'feeling' basis as well as on an ideas level was achieved, exhibiting the fact that they were persons and not a programme group; a sharing and not a telling group; a listening and not necessarily a leading group, as described by Robert Leslie in his *Sharing Groups in the Church*.

Within some groups some members abreacted their feelings about their isolation and loneliness, about their alienation from their own biological families, about difficulties that they had with other members of the church, the complaints about the services and various deficiencies which they found within the church. Others spoke about their own feelings of inadequacy and their defective faith and in this they were helped considerably by other members of the household. The household also supported those who were sick and one group in particular supported one member through his terminal illness.

Most of the groups had a missionary link in that they took specific interest in one missionary serving abroad and kept in touch with him or her, wrote regularly to him and gave him active support. When the missionary returned on furlough to this country, he or she would attend the household and thus it would become a supportive group to him or her while they were in the United Kingdom.

As already implied, it was always emphasised that these households of faith were an essential part of the church of St Mary's, and this link was further emphasised when members of the households would become responsible for some special task within the church. For example, on several occasions various households would become responsible for the prayers during public worship, and at other times they would become responsible for the music. If other tasks were necessary, such as taking part in welcoming visitors, then households would be nominated to do this.

A further link with the church itself was forged by the groups' taking up a theme which might have been the basis of a series of sermons by the clergy. For example, after a series of sermons on prayer the members of the groups discussed prayer, in its various aspects, for a number of months. The groups also gave an opportunity for those who had never prayed in public before to have an opportunity so to pray. This gave an opportunity in particular for young Christians to overcome their initial shyness and be able to learn to pray in a group and in public.

After the initial period of two years all the households were given the opportunity to express their views about the future. There was a clear consensus that they wished the households to continue for a further two years and remain in a similar mould to the first two-year period. This was a natural break and it gave an opportunity for some readjustment of the member groups and new members who had entered the church during the previous year or two, who were now in a position to be offered membership of the groups. Hardly any of the established members left the groups.

During this second term, now that they were firmly established, the households were prepared for outreach, and a number of groups took part in such activities. Some took part in specific evangelical meetings, others in going from door to door in the parish to greet the occupants, hand them literature concerning the work of St Mary's and invite them to attend the services, at the same time encouraging them to talk about any particular problem they might have. During the Christmas period the members of the households would go as groups to sing carols in various parts of the parish and again invite those who wished to talk to come to the church. In this way the church was able to make contact with people and families in the parish and as a result many people began to attend church for the first time or to recommence attending.

Above all, within the groups themselves, considerable spiritual growth occurred. Members began to practise true love between one another, were able to accept each other's difficulties and anger and aggressions and come to terms with them. In this way true growth occurred.

Every successful group proved to be just what Robert A. Edgar described in *The Listening Structured Group* thus, 'It is a laboratory of love where persons experience the giving and receiving of acceptance, forgiveness, understanding and concern. It is a group where persons go to listen with openness and positive interest, with sacrificial involvement; with expectancy so great as to evoke the fullest capacities for each other; with patience grounded in faith, what the person may become; and without judgment but with deep care.' The households of St Mary's became true growth cells and resource groups where there was undoubtedly striking maturing of individuals spiritually, and the forging of deep loving relationships.

We may well as a church be facing difficult times. It may well be that we are no longer a Christian nation and that it would be more appropriate to regard us as pagan. Suddenly there are numbers of people who have not even heard of Christ or of His church, let alone have any interest in it. There are others who actively oppose it and see no need for it. In increasing difficulties, economic and others of our time, the opposition may well grow fiercer and society be less tolerant towards those who follow Him. If that is so, these households of faith, these small groups, these cells, will become of paramount importance as a way of existence for Christians, and the only way to preserve a way of life and our faith in the face of increasing difficulties, hostility and even persecution.

B. WONDERFUL COUNSELLOR

18. WONDER OF A COUNSEL

This is the spirit, God's spirit, that runs throughout history and throughout the Bible. In the New Testament, when Jesus was about to leave His disciples, He promised them 'another counsellor', which was to be the Holy Spirit. His spirit was to be ever present with them and was to transform them from a group of apparently shipwrecked frightened men into a powerful group who would overturn the world.

This is the spirit which was within Christ Himself, 'The wonderful counsellor', the very name given by Isaiah in his prophecy regarding the coming of the Messiah. Christ was the fulfilment of the prophecy, the climax of God's revelation to man and the working of His spirit.

His spirit had been ever present from the beginning, from the creation of the world. When the earth was without form and void and darkness was upon the face of the deep, the spirit of God was moving over the face of the waters, says Genesis. God's spirit moves throughout the Old Testament and reveals Himself at striking moments in the history of Israel, God's chosen people. 'God saw Abraham and saw a nation in him.'

Throughout, the work of the spirit of God is always two-fold, He is a channel of prophecy, and He is the source of pastoral power and care. In Numbers, 11, God had 'taken back part of the same spirit that he had conferred on Moses and conferred it on the 70 elders' (v. 25). Against men who were absent at the time, who were later filled with the spirit and behaved in an ecstatic manner, the young men in the camp protested. Moses answered, 'I wish that all the Lord's people were prophets, and that the Lord would confer his spirit upon them all' (v. 29).

The word 'wonder' itself is first used in Exodus 15, in the song of Moses, which was sung by the victorious Israeli nation after the great deliverance from the bondage of Egypt. The Psalms take up the theme of God's 'wonder', His redemptive saving nature and His restoring power. David is acutely aware of the presence of the spirit. Psalm 139 speaks of His presence everywhere. Wherever man goes, whether he ascends or descends, the spirit of God will be there. This is a unique insight into the presence of God's spirit in the life of man. In Psalm 143:10 there is the same intimate sense of God's spirit directing and counselling man. 'Teach me to do your will, for you are my God. May your good spirit lead me on level ground.'

In Isaiah, the blending of prophecy and pastoral care reaches its height. Isaiah describes the qualities of Jehovah's previous acts in saving his people; these acts of wonder are merely forerunners of the most wonderful act of all, the unique redemptive act of sending of the Messiah. This was to be the wonder of wonders. The servant will 'make justice shine on every race', but he is also one 'who will not break a bruised reed or snap out a smouldering wick'. This is a highlight of the Old Testament insight, in the spirit of God as a caring spirit. In Isaiah 9:6, Isaiah predicts that Christ will be called 'counsellor – wonderful counsellor'.

There has been much discussion as to whether the two words form one title. It appears that, in spite of the gusto with which choirs have sung the 'Hallelujah Chorus', including 'wonderful, counsellor', they should really be treated as a pair, – 'Wonderful Counsellor'. S. T. Luzzatto takes the view that the eight words are one sentence and one title, while G. B. Bray takes the opposite view that all eight are separate titles. The Authorised Version translation regards words 3–8 as pairs, thus giving two single titles and three paired titles.

This is the view best known and brought to mind by Handel's *Messiah*. The Revised Standard Version, the New

American Standard Version and many modern commentators, view the eight words as four coupled titles. Thus we see the recent expositors favour the view that the Messiah should be considered 'a wonderful counsellor' or a 'wonder of a counsellor'.

The word 'counsellor' or 'adviser' is used earlier in the second book of Samuel 15:12, where Ahithophel is called David's 'counsellor'. Two kinds of counsellor appear in the Old Testament, namely the political adviser, such as Ahithophel, and the prophets. The latter bring God's counsel to His people. God's spirit continued to counsel the nation collectively throughout their period in the wilderness and had an ongoing dynamic relationship with them. He also counselled individual members of the community, such as Moses and Aaron. Jehovah counselled the nation through His servants, the prophets. His word was the 'wonder' given to His people through His messengers, the prophets. In spite of their mutterings and rebellion, God counselled them and supplied them with bread from heaven, manna, for forty years in the wilderness. Job's life is also an example of God's counselling of the individual. For all Job's sufferings he never lost touch with the God who counselled him. He shared the counsels of God and gained rich insights into His character to such an extent that he was able to utter the glorious words, 'I know my redeemer liveth' (Job 19:25).

In Isaiah 61, the climax of prophecy and pastoral caring is reached when the promises of the coming of the Messiah to an ungrateful people are given thus, 'The Spirit of the Lord God is upon me because the Lord has anointed me.' This spirit prophesied, proclaiming 'a year of the Lord's favour and a day of vengeance of our God.' The spirit also called for a caring, healing ministry, 'To bring good news to the humble, to bind up the broken hearted, to proclaim liberty to the captives.'

All this evidence from the Old Testament is building up a description of our Lord's own ministry to come on earth and to the ministry of His body, the church. The final pointer forward into New Testament fulfilment of all this, is Joel,

2:28–32. 'The day is coming when upon *all* flesh, the spirit will be outpoured. Young people shall prophesy, old people shall dream, young men have visions.'

In this universal vision there is focused all the hinting and discussing of the earlier insights into God's spirit in the Old Testament. Yet even here there is little to show of the graciousness and the power that was to come at Pentecost, nor the ways in which the spirit would work in revealing the Messiah and opening men's eyes to the Kingdom of God.

The Messiah is thus promised to come and His name will be called 'Wonderful Counsellor'. He will be the counsellor of counsellors, the true prophet-counsellor. He will reveal the whole wonder of God's mind and counsel. He is the great final prophet who brings God's word to His people (Deut. 18:18).

19. JESUS CHRIST –
'WONDERFUL COUNSELLOR'

By the words of God Himself He will be able to counsel His people perfectly as a nation and individually. He will be their shepherd and He will come alongside them and tell them of God's plans and words. This Messianic King, Supreme Counsel, will need no other advisers. He will need no intermediaries nor prophets. He will be God Himself in direct link with His people and the Holy Spirit will be upon Him (Isa. 11:1–3). He is the spirit of understanding and wisdom. He, being God, will know God's counsel. His spirit will be upon Him and He will be able to say, 'Thus God speaks.'

The Messianic King will be a wonder-counsellor, not only because He is God and brings God's words of counsel, but because He will accomplish the redemptive wonders and God's plans for salvation. He will come as God, break the barriers of place and time, take upon Him the flesh of man, be tempted in the same way as every man and yet remain without sin. He will be the one who Himself will experience and suffer as every other man.

He was the perfect counsellor in that He knew what was in men. He also knew God's mind. He also suffered, as man, the indignities of rejection by His own people. He had to experience and suffer the indignities of unorthodox birth, of rejection by His own people and the betrayal by His closest friends, the loneliness of Gethsemane as He struggled to make decisions about His own fate. Eventually He suffered misunderstandings, criticisms, the pettiness of people, disappointments, shared the hurts and sorrows of many people's hearts and carried the burden of their sins. 'Wonderful Counsellor' – can there be any doubt that Jesus Christ was fulfilment of the prophecy? He is the greatest counsellor that ever lived.

He accepted continual intrusions upon His privacy, had no respite from dawn to dusk. There was a steady drain on His spiritual resources and people broke in on His hours of quiet. He was prepared to share every hurt heart's burdens and sins and felt them as personally as if they were His own, yet He remained serene, showed no irritation and accepted men, though individuals and the crowds made demands upon Him. As already shown, He was supreme as counsellor. Some of His supreme counselling moments were those where He met individuals face to face, as with the woman of Samaria when He talked and discussed with her the true meaning of life, and Nicodemus, the local celebrity who came to Him at twilight.

There are numerous examples throughout His public ministry where Jesus counsels people – the frustrated invalid, the social snob, the petty protectionist, the crooked civil servant, the pillar of the establishment, the man of means, and so many who came to Him for healing, such as the woman in the crowd who touched Him and the blind beggar who cried to Him. He even counselled a dying criminal and brought him healing and salvation. And as the resurrected Lord, He cured the depression of the pair on the way to Emmaus. He counselled families as He did Martha, whom He believed was concerned with the trivial and petty things of this life, and brought succour and support to the Bethany family in the hour of greatest grief when Lazarus died. He even counselled the disciples when faced with a mass of thousands. Five thousand followed Him one day out to the secret retreat in the wilderness. When the disciples begged Him to send them away, He demanded that they gave them to eat because He saw them as sheep without a shepherd. 'And I love them.' He counselled His disciples again when they were in a state of panic one night on the murderous sea when they believed that as He slept He cared not that they might perish. Jesus calmed the waves and calmed their anxieties.

His word and counsel created the world: His word and counsel sustains it. His word brings peace, healing and salvation. Should we dare mention Freud, Jung, Adler, Horney, Klein, Sullivan, Fromm, Rank, Rogers, Maslow, Skinner,

Laing, Winnicott or any other psychiatrist in the same breath with Him? How long shall we seek the counsel of man alone when in Him we have the counsel of God?

Jesus Christ is the God – man who counsels. He has the power of life and death in His hands.

For three and a half years while on earth, during His public ministry, Jesus guided, rebuked, instructed, encouraged and taught His disciples and others. He was truly their counsellor, Wonderful Counsellor.

20. 'ANOTHER COUNSELLOR' – HOLY SPIRIT

As Jesus was about to leave His disciples, He graciously calmed their fears of the separation by informing them that He would send 'another counsellor', like Himself, to be with them, to teach and guide them as He had done previously. He identified this other counsellor as the Holy Spirit, the spirit of truth who would lead men to all truth and this truth would make them free.

The rendering 'comforter' goes back to Wycliffe, but the authoritative note written in the *Hastings Dictionary of the Bible*, Vol. 4, by Prof. Ivor Enoch, clearly shows that the technical name for the Holy Spirit in the church is *Parakletos* and is the past principle passive form of the basic Greek word which means 'to call someone to stand by your side', *Parakletos* thus being correctly translated 'someone who is called to stand by your side'. This is the very best definition one could find for counsellor, and here is the counsellor par excellence, the counsellor of counsellors.

Christian counselling inevitably means Jesus at the centre. Without Him we may and indeed can, as I have shown, have systems that are not necessarily Christian, though they are effective to a limited degree.

Christian counselling aims unashamedly to introduce the client to the great counsellor and leads to wholeness and salvation. He fills the gap left by all other counsellings. Jesus only can fill the gaps and threatening vacuums. It is often insufficient to remove the symptoms of discord and hurt at the basis of psychological symptoms for afterwards a void persists which can be filled by other problems and conflicts. Jesus can fill this gap for He is the creator of all things (John 1:3, Col. 1:16) and consequently knows all about men. He is the sustainer of all things (Heb. 1:3). He knows and cares about

what happens to people in the world (Eph. 1:11). He redeems
mankind; He reveals God's redemptive works and Himself
accomplishes them. 'By his stripes we are healed', and 'The
chastisement of us all is upon him' (Isa. 53:5). 'He without sin
was made sin for us' (2 Cor. 5:21).

21. CHRISTIAN COUNSELLING

I have shown the effectiveness and still emphasise the effectiveness of counselling in general, but have also shown the dangers of extreme client-centred therapy and selfism. We guard against this by placing Jesus Christ at the centre of all Christian counselling. Jesus Christ must be given His rightful place, worshipped even in the counselling room. To remove Jesus Christ from our counselling is to destroy the one ultimate hope that man has, for who but He by His cross conquered death, sin and the power of evil.

Some might ask how this matches up with my professional role. I have already attempted to answer this question by saying that within the N.H.S. we do general counselling but that in our own time, in a church setting where Christian counselling is done, then the good news of Jesus Christ is conveyed to the clients (Phil. 1:1–4) showing them that all true encouragement comes from Christ and that 'Jesus is the answer' to their problems. Man's chief purpose in life is to glorify God and enjoy Him for ever.

Christ is the author of peace, joy and love, which are beyond the understanding of the world. Herein there is an extra dimension. We don't merely conquer our symptoms and our disorders, but in Him we are more than conquerors. Again I stress that we do not start preaching to the counsellee before making contact and a relationship with him. Timing is all important, but it does mean that our practice must be consistent with our belief and that Christian counselling thus must be Christ centred, for we accept that he is the final solution to man's dilemma. It is only union with Him that leads to complete healing. While presenting Christ is not the only aspect of Christian counselling, Christian counselling can never be less than presenting Christ.

But this means that if union with Christ is the central aim of

Christian counselling, it follows inevitably that the Christian counsellor himself must have experienced that union in his own life; that Jesus Christ is his Saviour and Lord; that Jesus is all sufficient; that nothing can separate him from the love of Christ, that the counsellor's own desire is to know Him as Lord, walk closer to Him and see Him as the Rose of Sharon and Lily of the Valley.

His prayer is:

> Show me Thy face – one transient gleam,
> Of loveliness divine,
> And I shall never think or dream
> Of other love save Thine.

This is the first essential for a Christian counsellor or pastoral work, a personal relationship with Jesus Christ and the personal experience of regeneration by God's saving work in Christ. In addition, he must also have experienced the Holy Spirit's existence in his own life, be he clergy, doctor or layman. For Holy Spirit means Christ constantly with us, His spirit being present in us and through us, present in the counselling. As a counsellor will be working under the power of the Holy Spirit, so he himself is the vehicle used to bring the message to the counsellee. He must never forget that as a counsellor he can never cause regeneration, he cannot give repentance, he cannot open the eyes of the spiritually blind and he cannot give faith. The work of repentance, of the giving of the faith, is the work of the Holy Spirit.

The counsellor is but a co-worker with God; a midwife called to help sometimes in a difficult birth. Indeed, there are times when a counsellor's work meets with rejection, if not open hostility. If this happens, he should humbly accept the fact, shake the dust off his feet and move on, as Jesus commanded. For we must not be surprised at failure, especially when we are reminded of Christ's other words, that what is good for the master is good for the slave. It is a sad fact that our Lord Himself could only weep over Jerusalem when it rejected Him. Similarly, He could only grieve over the rich young ruler, though He loved him and found him an attractive personality, when he turned his back upon Him.

It is important to accept that the person becoming a Christian does not become whole immediately. The Christian isn't sanctified spontaneously. 'The universal renovation of our natures by the Holy Spirit into the image of God' doesn't happen immediately at a stroke, but is a process. Becoming a Christian doesn't simply mean that you accept that your sins are forgiven and that you are immediately reconciled to God. This is but a beginning. The Christian is a man who is 'born again'. We may be somewhat disillusioned to realise that regeneration does not alter our personality traits or get rid of our basic impulses immediately, if at all. Yet the Christian as a 'born again' person is a new man with a new mind, a new outlook and a new understanding. He has within him the Holy Spirit who will lead him into all truth and it is remarkable how we continually see lives change. The growth and maturing to the stature and measure of the Lord Jesus is a slow and painful progress and we change by degrees from glory to glory. Readers who face problems and feel that change takes place slowly, take heart. Paul had to remind the first-century Christians when he saw their struggles, of whom they were as new creatures in Christ: 'Know ye not that your bodies are the temple of the Holy Ghost' (1 Cor. 3:16). 'Behold all things are become new' (2 Cor. 5:17).

Surely, therefore, this is the only *complete* healing that can occur: Christian counselling under the guidance of the Holy Spirit alone can achieve it, but achieve it, it can.

Charles Wesley says this so eloquently in these beautiful words:

> Finish then Thy new creation,
> Pure and spotless let us be;
> Let us see thy great salvation,
> Perfectly restored in Thee;
> Changed from glory into glory,
> Till in heaven we take our place,
> Till we cast our crowns before Thee,
> Lost in wonder, love and praise.

As individuals and as nations, we are in the grip of great anxieties and fears. Individuals are in despair, lost in their neuroses, depressions and sin. Nations of the world are baffled, perplexed and without hope. Our aggressive, destructive powers become more evident daily as does man's inhumanity to man. This broken, warring world is in despair. We grope in the dark, we stand helpless before the towering mystery of evil's tragic dominion, including our hopeless inadequacy in the face of increasing destruction and worry. Psychiatry has helped and continues to help and can be effective in curing and alleviating much sickness.

But psychiatry must not obliterate the boundary between sickness and evil. We are still fighting the spectres of the night; we are still searching pathetically for some man-made humanistic solution to our problems, struggling in the morass of fear, of impotence and confusion. The supreme need of the world today is to start living in the light of the cross and to know the power of the resurrection and the Holy Spirit, while accepting God's empire of righteousness, peace, joy and liberty. It is by His blood we are cleansed and by His power we are resurrected. It is this same resurrection power which created the world and created man, which can create us anew.

That resurrection power can be ours today. Was there ever a transition more remarkable to explain in purely naturalistic and psychological grounds than that which, almost in the twinkling of an eye, carried Christ's abject, trembling followers from their lowest abyss of irrevocable despair to the sunlit heights of courage, conviction and confidence in the living God, and which led to the creation of a living church? The historian or theologian or doctor who thinks he can explain that in terms of psychological mechanisms or humanistic, non-supernatural theology is being simply non-scientific. 'This is the Lord's doing, and it is marvellous in our eyes.'

His touch has still its ancient power. This is God's decisive answer to the fears of the world; this Christ, the Wonderful Counsellor, is the answer. Everything any man may need is here – hope when all hope is broken, courage when you are terrified, light when you are in darkness, forgiveness when you have sinned, friendship when you are lonely and forsaken and, at the last, the wonderful welcome home to a new, eternal life from the Lord of life eternal.

Jesus Christ, Wonderful Counsellor – the same yesterday, today and for ever.

APPENDICES

APPENDIX A

INITIAL ASSESSMENT FORM

Abbreviated Scheme for Taking the Case History

1. Follow this format, but not slavishly.
2. Be concise, avoid jargon where possible. Emphasise what is important.
3. Keep the history and your assessment of the emotional state separate.
4. If possible, obtain a confirmatory history from a relative or acquaintance.
5. If a physical examination is indicated, ask to see general practitioner.

THE CASE HISTORY

    Patient's NAME: SEX: AGE:
             ADDRESS:
             OCCUPATION:
             MARITAL STATUS:
             RACE:

Complaints (or reason for referral)
    and their duration:

History of present complaint:
in coherent, chronological form

a) How long present?
b) How far life disrupted?
c) Change in appetite
d) Sleep and behaviour

Medical history:

a) Previous physical health. Allergies
b) Previous mental health, including prominent psychiatric symptoms for which treatment was *not* received
c) Any previous counselling

Family history:

a) Parents: *Father* – occupation, relationship
   Mother – if dead, for age of client
b) Siblings
c) Medical history: any familial illnesses
d) Home atmosphere and influence

Personal history:

a) Date and place of birth
   Any complications of pregnancy or delivery
b) Early development
c) Neurotic symptoms in childhood
d) Progress at school – primary, secondary, tertiary
e) Interests in games or sports during youth
f) Occupational history
g) Psychosexual development
   – Age of puberty
   Dating
   Engagement
   Marriage
   Children
h) Marriage

i) Children
j) Personal habits: Food; Sleep; Alcohol; Tobacco; Drugs. Note any change in habits
k) Antisocial history

Personality before illness:

a) Social relations; adequacy or otherwise in dealing with people
b) Activities, interests and hobbies
c) Normal mood state
d) Character
e) Personal standards
f) Normal energy and initiative
g) Religion: Active? Difficulties?

Current Social Circumstances:

a) Home
b) Finance

Any other information:

Always allow the client to state whether there is anything else he/she regards as important or relevant to his condition.

Current Emotional State:

a) General Behaviour and Appearance: Does client look dishevelled – or excessively tidy?
b) Mood: Elated? Depressed? Flat? Appropriate?
c) Form of (1) Talk
        (2) Thought – Is it possible to follow the train of thought?
d) Content of Thought
        (1) Ideas
        (2) Delusions
        (3) Obsessional phenomena

      (4) Phobias
  e) Hallucinations and other
    disorders of perception
  f) Cognition
      (1) Orientation – time,
       place and person
      (2) Memory: Any loss –
       recent or long
       term?
      (3) Attention and
       Concentration: Is
       client alert and
       in touch with
       surroundings?
      (4) General
       information – Ask
       simple questions
       such as the name of
       the Queen, Prime
       Minister
      (5) Intelligence –
       Assess from the
       interview, personal
       history and
       education
       achievement
  g) Insight and Judgment – Does
    patient know what is wrong
    and what the causes may be.

Provisional formu- Management and
lation, including treatment
secondary pro- a) Outline
blems: b) Aims and Duration

APPENDIX B

Basic Principles of Lay Counselling

1. INITIAL ASSESSMENT

On the basis of a full initial assessment the counsellor will find different needs.

    a) Some will be severely disturbed needing referral to a psychiatrist.

      e.g. i) Those with a history of psychosis

          ii) Those who are currently suicidal; drowsy and grossly disorientated with memory loss; those with thought disorder and delusions and/or hallucinations.

    b) Some will need to see their G.P.

      e.g. i) Those with a history of physical illness and with current physical symptoms.

         ii) Those with very low intelligence.

The remaining groups in general are likely to be suitable for counselling, but avoid those who have already had help from many other agencies without success.

    c) The most appropriate points:

      Young

      Good intelligence and education

      Well-motivated

      Symptoms causing suffering

      Working regularly

      Healthy family background

      Personal health record good

      Acute onset and short history

      Symptoms – neurotic or mild personality disorder

Secondary problems – solvable

Partner keen to help

N.B. The farther away from this ideal, the greater the hazards of counselling – the less favourable the prognosis.

2. APPROPRIATE ROOM

Comfortable room, sound-proof, well heated and ventilated, easy chairs, desk if required, soft lighting (preferable to have other persons in the building in case of any crisis).

3. CONTRACT

a) Agree on place, time, frequency of interviews and their length (usually one hour). Promptness expected of counsellor and client.

End interview at appointed time, although often at end of interview client will offer new exciting material.

Advise client to bring this subject up at next interview.

Remember that three one-hour interviews more valuable than one three-hour session.

And therapist's time limited – he has other commitments, including those to his own family.

And a client who can go on talking for several hours about his/her symptoms may well not be suffering much.

b) Agreement as to possible period of counselling, e.g. three months or six months or one year, although this can be modified.

c) First interview is very important:

N.B. Counsellor summing up client, and client summing up counsellor.

One interview sometimes enough to 'deal' with the problem posed.

Sometimes several interviews needed even to complete the assessment.

4. DO NOT OPEN WOUNDS YOU CANNOT CLOSE

i.e. Don't take on problems beyond your ability. Refer to others more able to deal with them.

5. DO NOT TAKE ON TOO MUCH TOO SOON

e.g. Giving hours of your time initially, at any hour of the day. Inevitably this will be reduced with the danger of the client's feeling greatly rejected. (A mistake of the inexperienced in their early enthusiasm.)

6. COUNSELLING TECHNIQUES – LISTENING

Listening – an essential ability.
Listening in such a manner as to instil confidence so that the client will talk freely about his real depth problems if he can identify them.
Listener must be accepting, non-judgmental, although he must never collude with wrong patterns of behaviour.
N.B. When a client says 'I'm going to tell you something I've never told anyone before', it means that you are being an effective listener.
N.B. Silences can be eloquent, though difficult to tolerate, especially at first. When touching a deep emotional problem, feelings may be shown before words are uttered to describe the underlying conflict.
Therefore learn to listen in silence.
Note the non-verbal forms of communication: smile, movements, posture, walk.

7. TECHNIQUES

Empathy
To be able to put yourself in the place of the client. Sympathy +. Linked must be feeling of warmth and a real understanding so that the client knows and feels you want

to help in a constructive manner, although it will be the client who will have to do most of 'the work'.

Work through the conflicts.

Be wary of too much positive feeling of love: refer to some other counsellor.

Be wary of too much positive feeling of anger and hatred: refer to some other counsellor.

8. COUNSELLING does not end in the counselling room.

Homework must be done by the client to try to manipulate environment to remove obvious stress. Cultivate relationships, consider the new insights gained and put into action new patterns of behaviour.

Counselling does not mean usurping the clients' powers but to make them more powerful to make their own decisions.

9. CONFIDENTIALITY

No gossip. No passing on of information gleaned in counselling session with any other person.

If notes are kept, must be under lock and key, with entries carefully made.

10. COUNSELLING has an *ending*

Ending the counselling can be difficult. Parting is sweet sorrow and some may want to continue beyond the agreed time. Others will be angry at the end.

Some will gradually drift away, unable to make a clear break.

Others will be pleased to stop treatment, feeling able to stand on their own.

11. SUPERVISION, especially initially and, indeed, even when you have found a great deal of expertise. There is a

need for sharing with someone more proficient and experienced.

If difficulties occur, refer early rather than late to the supervisor.

This can be done by direct 'phone call to the supervisor, when you meet him individually, or in a group; the meetings should be regular.

Such meetings with other counsellors will help to give you support and keep you abreast of developments.

12. SIDE-EFFECTS as with every other form of treatment.

Addicted to it – not wanting to end the counselling and if pressed looks elsewhere for more.

Failures – must be prepared for failure; i.e. no progress; often ingratitude, even in successful counselling; sometimes there may be complaints about various aspects of your counselling – even from those you have helped most.

13. COUNSELLING is hard work, but can be very rewarding in helping to restore shattered personalities.

It is part of the wider *Healing Ministry*.

GLOSSARY

ABREACTION – A process by which repressed material, particularly a painful experience of a conflict, is brought back to consciousness. In the process of abreacting the person not only recalls but relives the repressed material, which is accompanied by the appropriate emotions.

AFFECT – MOOD – Feelings and emotions usually attached to ideas.

AFFECTIVE DISORDERS – Illness in which a mood change is the primary or dominant feature.

AGORAPHOBIA – Fear of open spaces. Can be severely disabling.

ALCOHOLICS – Those persons whose drinking interferes with their physical or mental health, their personal relationships or their working ability. This definition includes, but is not restricted to, those persons physically dependent on alcohol. An alternative term is 'problem drinkers'.

AMBIVALENCE – Presence of strong and often overwhelming simultaneous contrasting attitudes, ideas, feelings, and drives towards an object, person or goal.

AMNESIA – Disturbance in memory manifested by partial or total inability to recall past experiences.

ANOREXIA NERVOSA – A distorted attitude to body weight and fatness with deliberate restriction of eating with the aim of drastic slimming. Often associated with secret disposal of food and vomiting and excessive use of laxatives. Episodes of over-eating may occur. Relationships with parents often disturbed. Usually takes fluctuating courses over several years and may leave long-lasting abnormal eating habits. May endanger life.

ANXIETY – An emotional state characterised by apprehension, uncertainty, dread, anticipatory fear.

ANXIETY NEUROSIS – The neurotic illness in which pronounced anxiety is the dominating feature.

AUDITORY HALLUCINATION – False auditory sensory perception.

AURA – The warning sensations that an epileptic may feel just before a seizure.

AUTISTIC THINKING – Retreating from realistic thinking to fantasy thinking, with the thoughts controlled exclusively by the thinker.

BEHAVIOUR THERAPY – A type of therapy that focuses on overt and objectively observable behaviour rather than on thoughts and feelings. It aims at symptomatic improvement and the elimination of suffering and maladaptic habits. Various conditioning and anxiety-eliminating techniques derived from learning theory are combined with didactive discussions and techniques adapted from other systems of treatment.

CLOUDING OF CONSCIOUSNESS – A mental state in which clear mindedness is impaired and orientation partially lost.

COGNITION – PERCEPTION – Awareness of perception. Knowing.

COMA – A state of unconsciousness so profound that the patient cannot be aroused.

COMPULSIVE PERSONALITY – A type of personality characterised by rigidity, over-conscientiousness, extreme inhibition, and inability to relax.

CONATION – That part of a person's mental life concerned with his strivings, instincts, drives and wishes, as expressed through his or her behaviour.

CONFLICT – A painful emotional state arising from tension between two opposed contradictory wishes.

DEJA VU – Illusion of visual recognition in which a new situation is incorrectly regarded as a repetition of a previous experience.

DELIRIUM (acute brain syndrome) – A mental state characterised by an impaired state of consciousness that stems from an acute organic illness typified by restlessness, confusion, disorientation, bewilderment, agitation and rapidly changing emotions. It is associated with fear, hallucinations and illusions.

DELIRIUM TREMENS (D.T.s) – An acute delirium (confusional state) occurring when alcohol is withdrawn from a person who is physically dependent.

DELUSION – A false, unshakable belief, which is out of keeping with the patient's personal, social and cultural background.

DEMENTIA (chronic brain syndrome) – Global deterioration of mental functioning due to physical changes to the brain, characterised by loss of recent memory, poor comprehension, emotional lability and tendency to self-neglect.

DEPRESSIVE ILLNESS – Distinguished from the normal experience of depression by being severe, persistent and disabling. Reactive depression is related to severe external stresses and/or a vulnerable personality. It is usually understandable. Endogenous depression has little or no external stress, comes 'out of the blue' and usually affects weight, sleep and drive. Assessment of suicidal risk is essential.

DRUG DEPENDENCE – A state, psychological and sometimes physical, resulting from the interaction of an organism and a drug, characterised by behaviour and other responses that always include a compulsion to take the drug on a continuous or periodic basis in order to experience its psychic effects and sometimes to avoid the discomfort of its absence. The tolerance may or may not be present. A person may be dependent on more than one drug.

DYSPAREUNIA – Physical pain in sexual intercourse, experienced by women; the cause may be physical or emotional.

ECSTASY – Intense feeling of elation, well-being and pleasure.

ELECTRO-CONVULSIVE THERAPY (E.C.T.) – A form of treatment empirically found to be of value in severe depression and some forms of schizophrenia. The patient is anaesthetised and muscles are relaxed. An electric charge then induces a controlled minimal epileptic fit.

ELECTRO-ENCEPHALOGRAM (E.E.G.) – A paper recording of the electrical activity of the brain obtained by a painless procedure during which electrodes are attached to the scalp.

EMOTIONS (affects) – Feelings with accompanying physical aspects and expressive behaviour. An individual with disturbed emotions may complain only of the physical aspects.

ENCOPRESIS – Passage of stools by children at inappropriate times and places – usually due to poor training or emotional upsets.

ENURESIS – Involuntary micturition (incontinence) by day (diurnal) or night (nocturnal) after an age when control would be expected. Primary – failure ever to acquire control – usually familial. Secondary – loss of acquired control – may be emotional.

EXHIBITIONISM – Term applied in psychiatry to persons who obtain sexual pleasure from exposing their genital organs to other people. In everyday living it means 'showing off'.

EXTROVERT – One whose personality type is characterised by an overt or outward display.

FLEXIBILITAS CEREA – Waxy flexibility. A condition in which the body and limbs of the patient will remain in the position in which they have been placed. Occurs in catatonic schizophrenia.

FLIGHTS OF IDEAS – A rapid succession of thoughts with no rational connection. Typically occurs in manic psychosis.

HALLUCINATIONS – Perceptions without an adequate external stimulus.

HOLISTIC – A term used in psychiatry to refer to the study of an individual as a distinctive entity rather than as a collection of various characteristics.

HYPOMANIA – A fixed change in mood when the patient is excited, elated, feels very well, and may have grandiose ideas. The mood is out of keeping with the circumstances.

HYSTERIA – Mental disorders in which motives (of which the patient seems unaware) produce a restriction of the field of consciousness or disturbance of motor or sensory function. These may seem to have a psychological advantage or symbolic value. May present as *conversion symptoms*, e.g. paralysis, tremor, blindness, aphonia (loss of voice), fits, without obvious physical cause. May present as *dissociation*, e.g. selective amnesia. The underlying cause of hysteria may be a psychological stress *or* a physical illness.

ILLUSIONS – Misinterpretation of stimuli arising from an external object.

INSIGHT – Awareness of one's own mental condition or of a situation.

INTELLIGENCE – Ability to perform mental tasks.

INTROVERT – One whose personality type is characterised by introspection and direction of interest inwards. A shy personality.

I.Q. Intelligence Content – A person's score on an intelligence test, compared with scores of a reference group, expressed in the formula

$$I.Q. = \frac{M.A.}{C.A.} \times 100$$

Where M.A. is mental age and C.A. is chronological age.

LABILE – Unstable; characterised by rapidly changing emotions.

LEUCOTOMY – An operation to cut some nerve fibres passing to the frontal lobes of the brain. Used in severe, intractable and disabling tension states. Falling out of use because of irreversibility, replacement by other treatments and danger of permanent personality change.

LIBIDO – Term used to denote sex drive or energy; or the sum of the vital force of energy that motivates life adjustments.

MAJOR TRANQUILLISERS – (neuroleptics) used in treatment of psychotic illness and severe agitation, e.g. chlorpromazine (Largactil).

MALINGERER – One who consciously simulates symptoms and pretends to be ill.

MANNERISM – A rapidly performed, semi-automatic gesture or grimace often seen in schizophrenia.

M.A.O.I.s – (Mono-amine oxidase inhibitors), a group of antidepressant drugs. Less commonly used because of serious interactions with certain drugs and certain foods (e.g. cheese). Example – phenelzine (Nardil).

NEUROSIS – Problems of definition despite wide use of this term. Present as anxiety, depression, phobias, hysterical symptoms, obsessional symptoms. The person can distinguish between his subjective experiences and external reality. Behaviour may be greatly affected but usually remains within socially accepted limits. The psychodynamic explanation is conflict, perhaps unconscious. The learning theory explanation is a learned habit in a susceptible individual who has been exposed to stress and therefore has had the opportunity to learn the neurosis.

NIHILISM – Rejection of beliefs, religious and moral.

NIHILISTIC DELUSIONS – Denial of existence of parts of or whole body.

NORMALITY – Concepts of 1 the average, 2 the ideal, 3 the statistical normal curve, 4 the absence of signs and symptoms of abnormality, 5 the continuous process of adjustment and adaptation (and possibly development). *All* concepts used in psychiatry and can be misleading.

OBSESSIONS – Unwanted thoughts which are perceived by the person as inappropriate. Efforts to dismiss the thoughts may lead to anxiety. Certain actions may be performed to relieve anxiety, e.g. washing hands.

PARANOID STATE – Ranges from ideas of being done down and put upon to mental disorganisation characterised by systemised delusions and hallucinations, often of a persecutory nature.

PERSONALITY – The unique, sum total of a person's psychological and physical characteristics. The established and largely unchanging patterns of relating to, perceiving, thinking and feeling about the environment and oneself. Abnormal personalities have patterns which are severely maladaptive and impair functioning and may have an adverse effect upon the individual and/or society. Psychopathic personality is an extreme form of abnormal personality.

PHOBIA – Anxiety inappropriately linked with an object or situation.

PRIMARY GAIN – The reduction of tension or conflict through neurotic illness.

PSYCHIATRIST – A medically qualified doctor who specialises in psychological medicine or psychiatry.

PSYCHIATRY – A branch of medicine dealing with the study, diagnosis and treatment of the abnormal functioning of all aspects of human behaviour – thinking, feeling, willing, acting.

PSYCHOANALYSIS – Term used for both Freud's method of psychic investigation and a form of psychotherapy. As a technique for exploring the mental processes, psychoanalysis includes the use of free association and the analysis and interpretation of dreams, resistances and transferences. As a form of psychotherapy it uses the investigative technique, guided by Freud's libido and instinct theories and by ego psychology, to gain insight into a person's unconscious motivations, conflicts and symbols. Requires specially trained therapists and involves extremely prolonged treatment.

PSYCHOLOGIST – A graduate psychologist with further training in diagnosis and treatment of psychiatric illness, emotional problems and mental subnormality. May use psychotherapy and/or behavioural treatments and specialised assessment techniques. Not medically qualified.

PSYCHOPATHOLOGY – The science which investigates and seeks to trace and understand the mental factors, influences, mechanisms and phenomena occurring in mental disorder.

PSYCHOSIS – Problems of definition despite wide use of this term. Impairment of mental function particularly in loss of contact with reality. Lack of ability to distinguish subjective experience from external reality. Presents as hallucinations, delusions, abnormal thinking processes, odd behaviour, reduced ability to cope with ordinary demands of life, loss of drive, inability of a person to recognise he is ill when this is obvious to others.

PSYCHOSOMATIC DISORDER – A physical disorder which is aggravated or precipitated by emotional disturbance.

PSYCHOTHERAPY – 'Talking treatment'. The treatment by psychological means of problems of an emotional nature in which a trained person deliberately establishes a professional relationship with a patient with the object of 1 removing or modifying symptoms (*supportive* psychotherapy) or 2 modifying disturbed patterns of behaviour (*re-educative* psychotherapy) or 3 promoting development of the full potential of the personality (*reconstructive* psychotherapy, psychoanalytic treatment).

PSYCHOTROPIC DRUGS – Those drugs having powerful effects on the central nervous system and used in psychiatric treatment.

SCHIZOID PERSONALITY – A shut-in, unsocial, shy type of personality, with a tendency to fantasise and with inadequate emotional involvement.

SCHIZOPHRENIA – A group of mental disorders with no coarse brain damage. Cannot be understood as arising emotionally or rationally from affective states, previous personality or current situation. There is characteristic interference with thinking, emotions, drive and motor behaviour. Schizophrenia is one form of psychosis.

SECONDARY GAIN – The obvious advantage that a person gains from his illness, such as gifts, attention and release from responsibility.

SELECTIVE INATTENTION – An aspect of attentiveness in which a person blocks out those areas that generate anxiety.

THERAPEUTIC ATMOSPHERE – All therapeutic, maturational and growth supporting agents – cultural, social and medical.

THERAPEUTIC COMMUNITY – Ward or hospital treatment setting where frequent and regular meetings of patients and staff aim to improve awareness in patients of their effects on others, to encourage communication, to lessen the hierarchical authority of staff over patients and to share responsibility for each other's care. In practice may help and tolerate some personality disorders not influenced by other forms of psychiatric care.

TRANSFERENCE – The emotional attitude the patient develops towards the psychiatrist in deep psychotherapy treatment.

TRANSVESTISM – Sexual gratification by wearing clothes of the opposite sex. Distinct from and not necessarily associated with homosexuality.

TRAUMA – A wound or injury, usually physical but can be mental, and is an emotional shock.

TRICYCLICS – Commonly used and effective group of anti-depressant drugs, e.g. imipramine (Tofranil).

UNCONSCIOUS – Thoughts, feelings, impulses which are not immediately available to the attention but nevertheless influence behaviour. Evidence for this in everyday life from verbal lapses, dreams and forgetting, indicating a part of the personality not immediately accessible to consciousness.

FURTHER READING

I THE HURT MIND

Introductory Reading In Psychiatry
1. PSYCHIATRY TODAY by D. Stafford-Clark. Penguin 1963.
2. PSYCHIATRY by E. W. Anderson and (revised by) W. H. Trethowan. Ed. Bailliere 1979.
3. A SHORT TEXTBOOK OF PSYCHIATRY by W. Linford Rees. London: Hodder and Stoughton 1976.
4. INTRODUCTION TO PSYCHOLOGICAL MEDICINE by D. Curran, Partridge and Storey. 9th Ed. Churchill-Livingstone 1980.
5. U.C.H. NOTES ON PSYCHIATRY. Ed. R. Tredgold and H. Wolff. 2nd Ed. 1980.
6. CLINICAL PSYCHIATRY IN PRIMARY CARE by S. L. Dubovsky and M. P. Weissberg. Baltimore: Williams & Wilkins 1978.

More Detailed Guides to Clinical Psychiatry
7. FISH'S CLINICAL PSYCHOPATHOLOGY. Ed. Max Hamilton. Bristol: John Wright & Co., 1967. Revised reprint 1974.
8. INSANITY. Ed. Robert G. Priest. G. Macdonald & Evans 1977.

Other General Reading
9. THE PSYCHOLOGY OF INSANITY by B. Hart. Camb. Univ. Press. 1962
10. THE INTEGRITY OF PERSONALITY. A. Storr. London: Heinemann 1960.
11. PSYCHIATRY AND ANTI-PSYCHIATRY by D. Cooper. Paladin 1967.
12. THE MYTH OF MENTAL ILLNESS. Thomas S. Szasz. Paladin 1972.

II THE TALKING CURES

Books On Counselling, Psychotherapy and Pastoral Care

13. PRINCIPLES OF PASTORAL COUNSELLING by R. S. Lee. London: S.P.C.K., 1968.
14. BASIC TYPES OF COUNSELLING by Howard Clinebell. Nashville: Abingdon, 1966.
15. THE BASIC STEPS TOWARDS CHRISTIAN MATURITY Ed. William Bright. California: Campus Crusade, 1965.
16. A GUIDE TO PASTORAL CARE by R. E. O. White. London: Pickering and Inglis, 1976.
17. PASTORAL CARE FOR LAY PEOPLE by Frank Wright. S.C.M.
18. PSYCHOLOGY AND LIFE by L. Weatherhead. Hodder and Stoughton, 1961.
19. PRESCRIPTION FOR ANXIETY by L. Weatherhead. Hodder and Stoughton, 1956.
20. PSYCHOLOGY, RELIGION AND HEALING by L. Weatherhead. Hodder and Stoughton, 1963.
21. COMPETENT TO COUNSEL by Jay E. Adams. Michigan: Baker Book House, 1977.
22. HANDBOOK OF PSYCHOTHERAPY AND BEHAVIOUR CHANGE by S. L. Garfield and A. E. Bergin. 2nd Ed. John Wiley & Sons, 1978.
23. INTRODUCTION TO PSYCHOTHERAPY. Ed. S. Bloch. Oxford Univ. Press, 1979.
24. ELEMENTS OF PSYCHOTHERAPY by A. J. Enelow. Oxford Univ. Press, 1977.
25. THE ART OF PSYCHOTHERAPY by A. Storr. London: Secker and Warburg, 1979.
26. PSYCHOTHERAPY: A PERSONAL APPROACH by D. J. Smail. London: Dent, 1978.
27. RESTORING THE IMAGE (An introduction to Christian Counselling) by R. E. Hurding, 1980.
28. A GUIDE TO COUNSELLING AND BASIC PSYCHOTHERAPY by R. Parry. London: Churchill-Livingstone, 1975.

III 'WONDERFUL COUNSELLOR'

29. YOUR HEALING IS WITHIN YOU by J. Glennon. London: Hodder and Stoughton, 1978.

30. THE CHURCH IS HEALING by M. Wilson. London: S.C.M., 1966.

31. GO PREACH THE KINGDOM HEAL THE SICK by J. Wilson. London: Clarke, 1963.

32. HEALING by F. MacNutt. Indiana: Ave Maria Press, 1974.

33. THE HEART OF HEALING by G. Bennett. Worcs.: James, 1974.

34. THE VARIETIES OF CHRISTIAN EXPERIENCE by W. James. London: Longmans, Green & Co., 1928.

35. A FAITH THAT ENQUIRES by Sir M. Jones. Gifford Lectures, 1922.

36. THEOLOGY AND SANITY by F. J. Sheed. London: Sheed-Ward, 1948.

37. THE CHRISTIAN PHYSICIAN IN THE ADVANCE OF SCIENCE AND THE PRACTICE OF MEDICINE. Ed. A. M. Connell and G. A. Linde Boom. Hague: A. J. Orange, 1966.

38. ROLE OF RELIGION IN MENTAL HEALTH. Ed. J. Taylor. London: NAMH 1967.

39. PSYCHIATRY AND RELIGION by S. Klausner. London: Collier-McMillan, 1964.

40. PSYCHIATRY AND CATHOLICISM by James H. Vander Veldt and R. P. Odennald. 2nd Ed.

41. CHRISTIAN ESSAYS IN PSYCHIATRY by Ed. P. Mainet. London: SCM, 1956.

42. THE DOCTOR AND THE SOUL by V. Frankl. Penguin Books, 1973.

43. SOUL AND PSYCHE by V. White. London: Collins, 1959.

44. GOD – THE UNCONSCIOUS by V. White, Fontana, 1960.

INDEX

Martin Israel

THE SPIRIT OF COUNSEL

The Holy Spirit is central in the work of the counsellor, argues the author. 'The spirit of counsel imparts power and instruction to those in need, and it is the primary function of the counsellor to be open to God in prayer so that the word that releases his clients from the bondage of fear and invidious past attitudes may be uttered definitively and with authority.'

Martin Israel is author of PRECARIOUS LIVING, SMOULDERING FIRE and THE PAIN THAT HEALS. He has been described by the *Church Times* as 'one of the most sought-after spiritual guides in this country.'